Reteach

Annotated Teacher's Edition

Level 1
Book 1

Columbus, OH

SRAonline.com

Printed in the United States of America.

Send all inquiries to this address:
SRA/McGraw-Hill
4400 Easton Commons
Columbus, OH 43219

ISBN: 978-0-07-610388-1
MHID: 0-07-610388-9

3 4 5 6 7 8 9 BCH 13 12 11 10 09 08 07

The McGraw·Hill Companies

Unit 1 Back to School

Unit 2 Where Animals Live

Unit 3 I Am Responsible!

Our Neighborhood at Work

Unit 5 What's the Weather?

Unit 6 North, South, East, West

Name ______________________ Date ________

Sounds and Spellings

Directions: Practice writing s and S. Then, draw two pictures whose names begin with the /s/ sound.

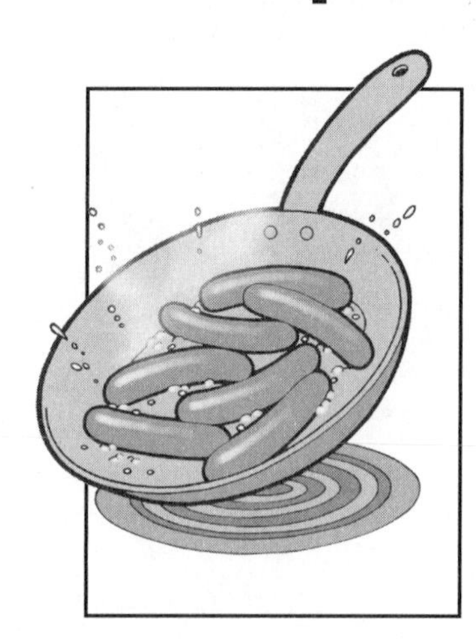

s

Practice A

s s s s s

S S S S S

1. Answers will vary. Picture must begin with the /s/ sound.

2. Answers will vary. Picture must begin with the /s/ sound.

Practice B

Directions: Say the name of each picture. Write a capital S next to each picture that begins with the /s/ sound.

3.

S

4.

S

5.

6.

S

7.

S

8.

S

Name ______________________ Date ________

Sounds and Spellings

Directions: Practice writing *m* and *M*. Then, draw two pictures that begin with the /m/ sound.

Practice A

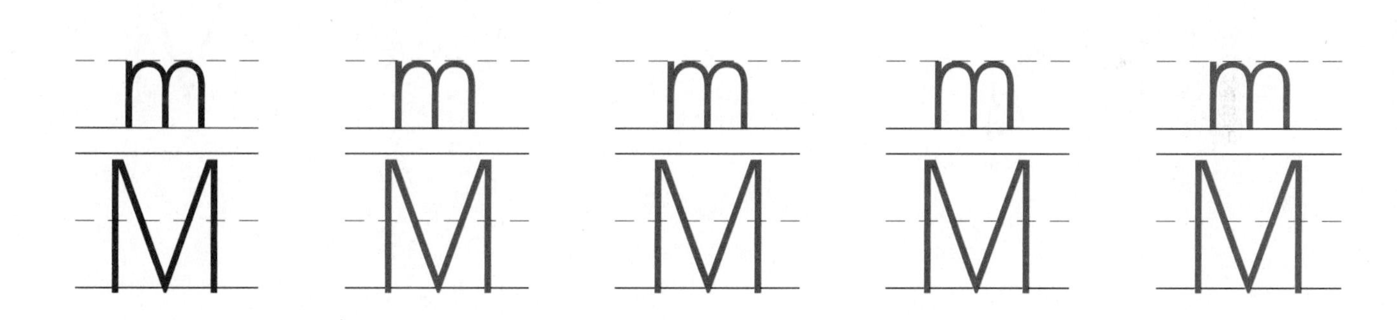

1. Answers will vary. Picture must begin with the /m/ sound.

2. Answers will vary. Picture must begin with the /m/ sound.

Practice B

Directions: Write a capital *M* on the line if the picture begins with the /m/ sound.

3.

4.

5.

6.
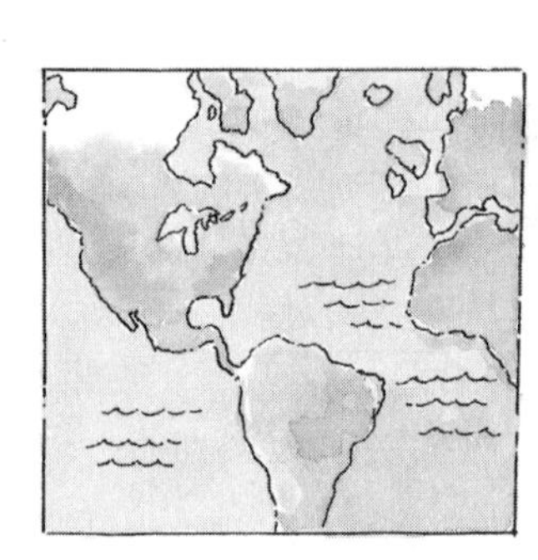
M

7.

M

8.

M

Name ______________________ Date ________

Sounds and Spellings

Directions: Practice writing a and A. Then name each picture and color the ones that have the /a/ sound.

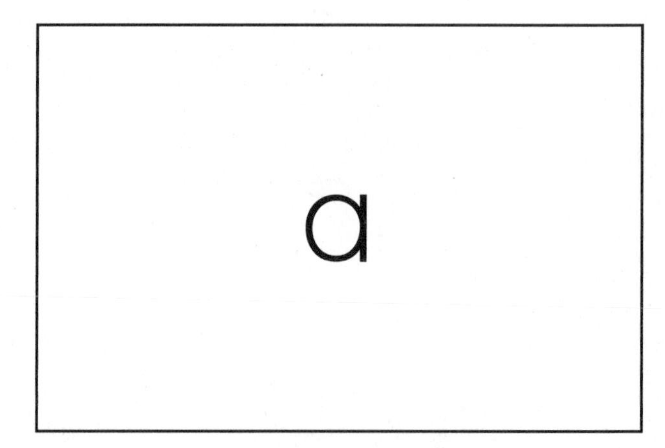

Practice A

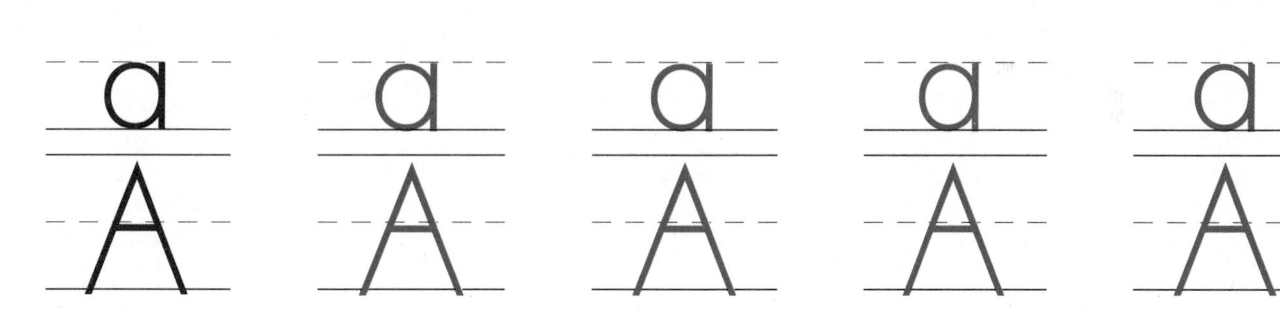

1. 2. 3.

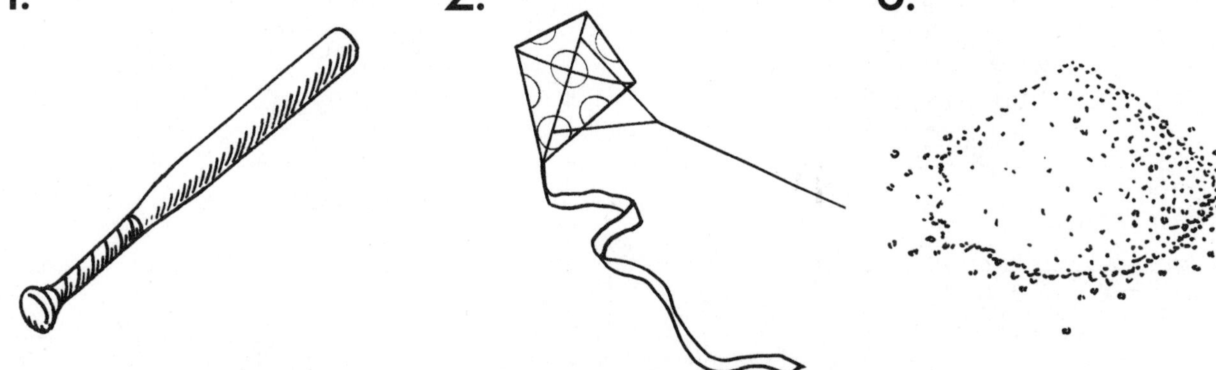

Students should color the bat and the sand.

Practice B

Directions: Write *a* on the line if the picture has the /a/ sound.

4.

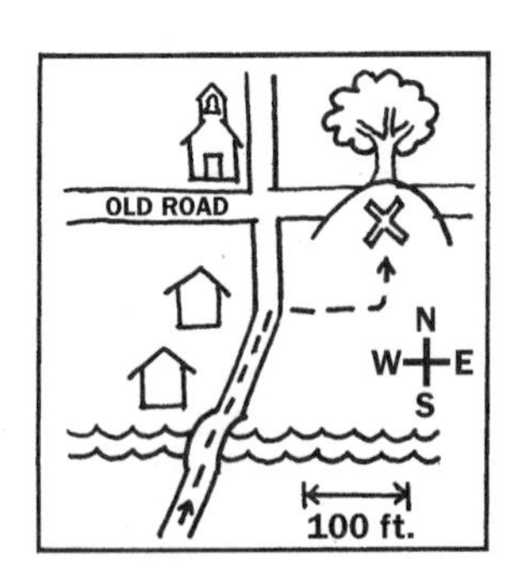

a

5.

a

6.

7.

a

8.

9.

a

UNIT 1 Lesson 3

Name ______________________ Date ________

Letters, Words, and Sentences

Focus

Letters	A a B b C c
Words	am mat the
Sentence	I am on the mat.

Practice A

Directions: Circle the word in each line.

1. m 

2. the e

3. have v

4. u 

5. see ee

6. on o

Practice B

Directions: Draw a line under each sentence. At the bottom of the page, count the number of words in the sentence. Circle the correct number.

7. Sam

I am Sam.

8. Sam Sam Sam

I can see Sam.

9. There is Sam the ___.

There There

10. I can see Sam up there.

5 (6) 7

Name ______________________ Date ________

Directions: Practice writing *t* and *T*. Copy the words on the lines.

Sounds and Spellings

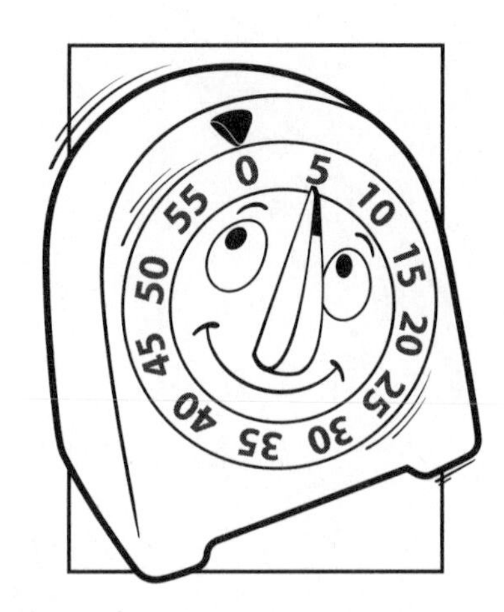

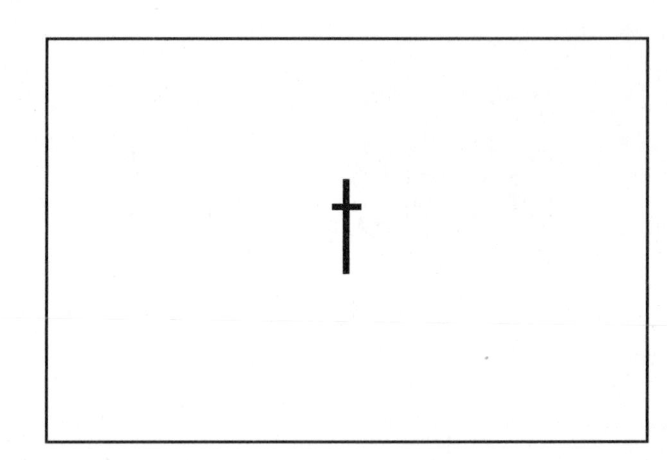

Practice A

t t t t t

T T T T T

sat sat mat mat

Lesson 4

Practice B

Directions: Say the name of each picture. Write capital T on the line if the picture begins with the /t/ sound.

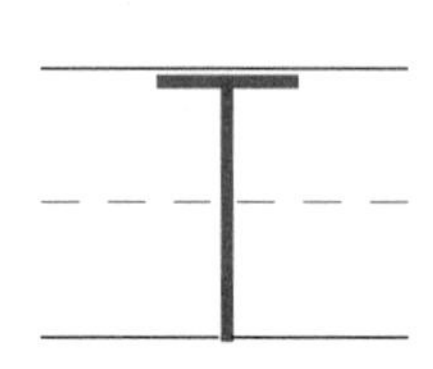

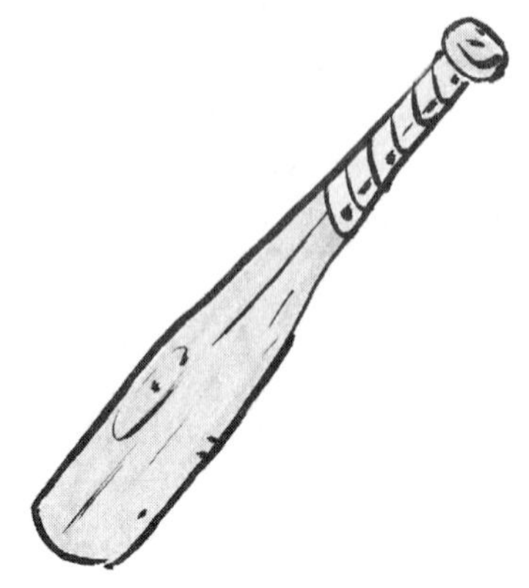

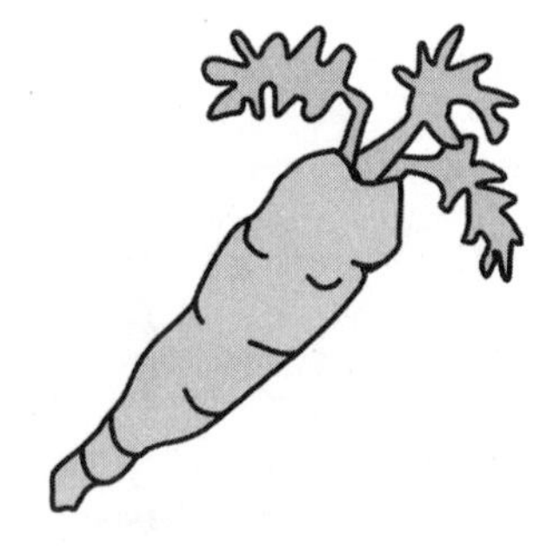

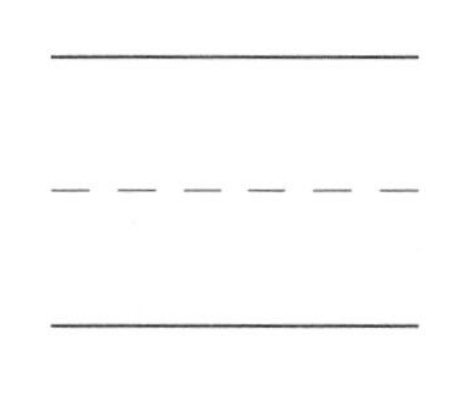

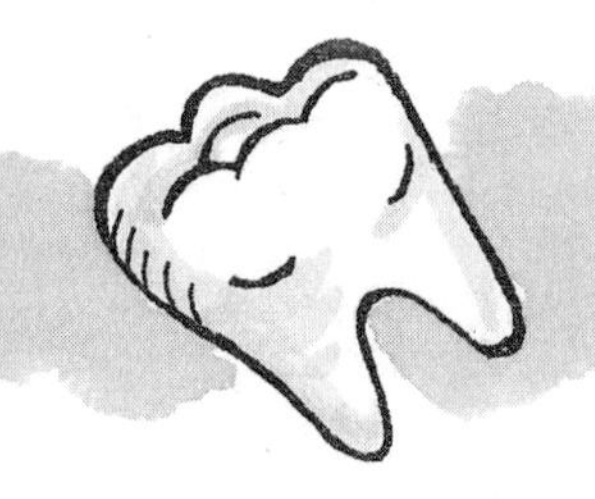

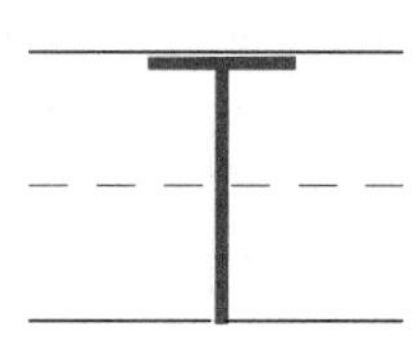

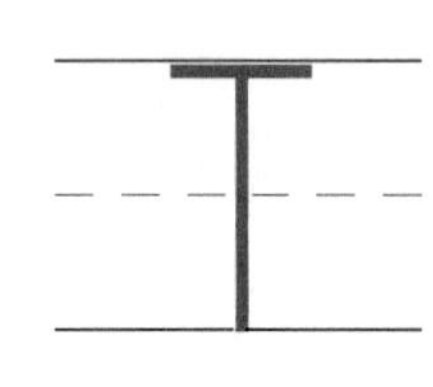

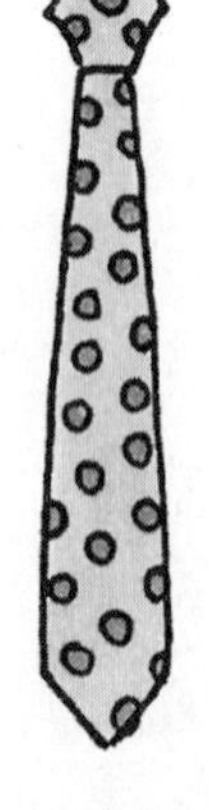

Name ______________________ **Date** ________

Sounds and Spellings

Practice A

Directions: Say the name of each picture. Write the spelling for the sound you hear at the beginning of each word.

1. 

s

2. 

m

3. 

a

4. 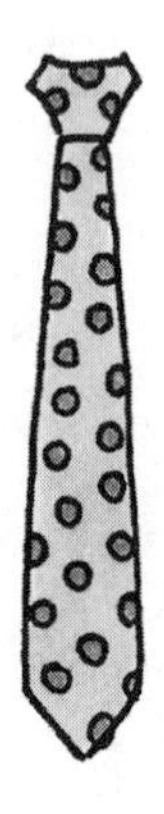

t

5. 

s

6. 

a

Practice B

Directions: Play *Riddle Me This!* Say the sound for each card. Write the spelling for each sound. Then say the sound for each one. Blend them together to make a word. Write the word on the line.

7.

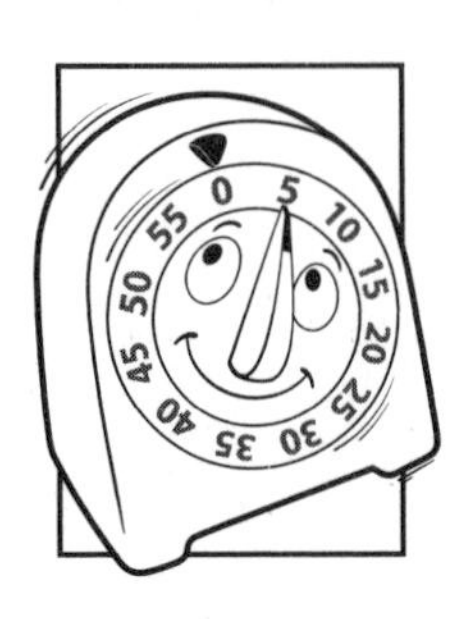

sat

s a t

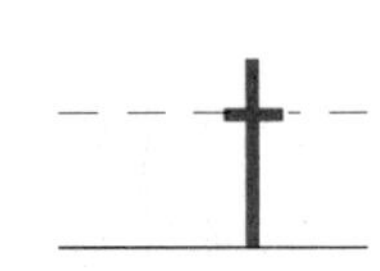

8.

am

a m

9.

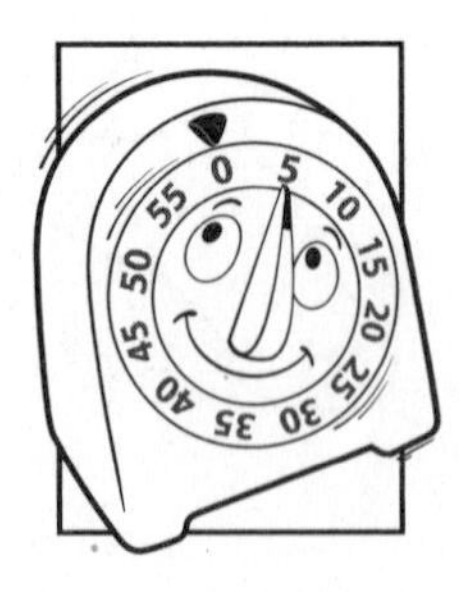

mat

m a t

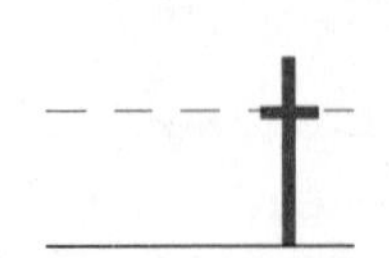

Name ______________________ Date ________

Sounds and Spellings

Directions: Practice writing *d* and *D*. Copy the words.

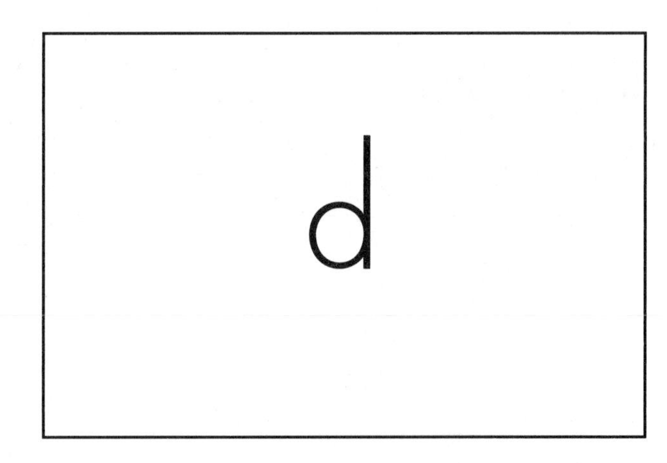

Practice A

d d d d d

D D D D D

dad dad sad sad

UNIT 1 Lesson 6

Practice B

Directions: Read each sentence. Look at the pictures. Draw a line from the sentence to the picture it matches.

1. Matt can add.

2. Sam is sad.

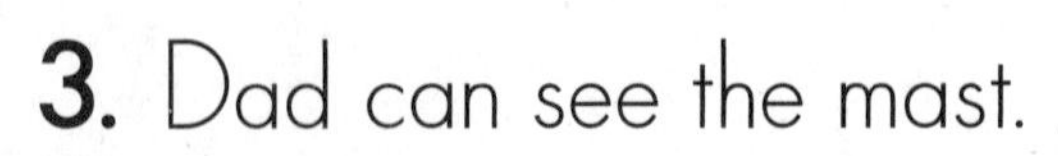

3. Dad can see the mast.

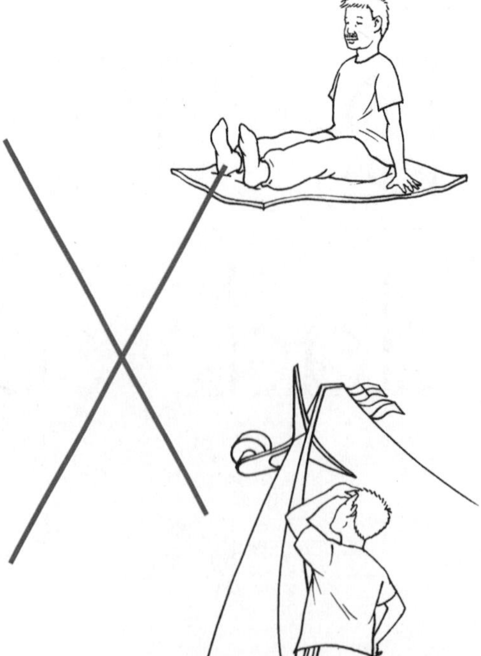

4. Dad sat on the mat.

Name ______________________ **Date** ________

Sounds and Spellings

Directions: Practice writing *n* and *N*. Then, draw two pictures whose names begin with the /n/ sound.

n

Practice A

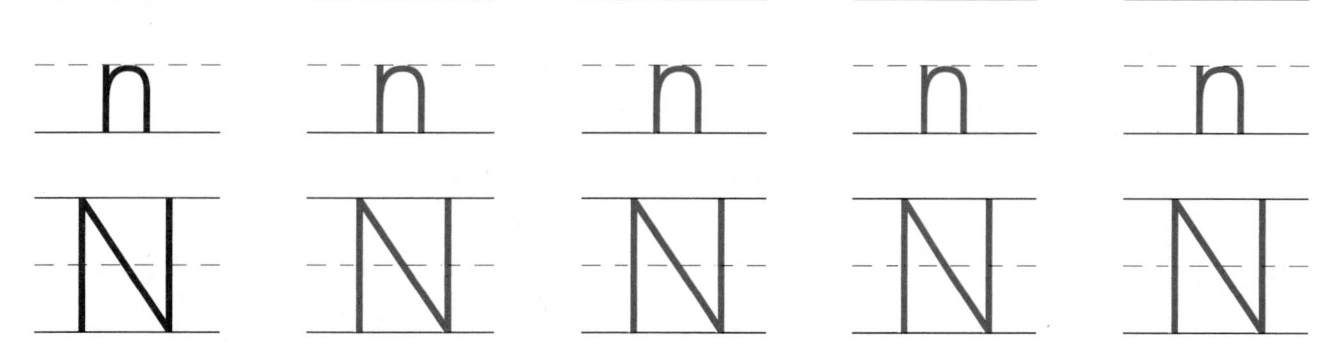

1. Answers will vary. Picture must begin with the /n/ sound.

2. Answers will vary. Picture must begin with the /n/ sound.

Practice B

Directions: Look at each picture and circle the correct word to finish each sentence.

3. 

Nan is on ____.

4. 

I am a ____.

5. 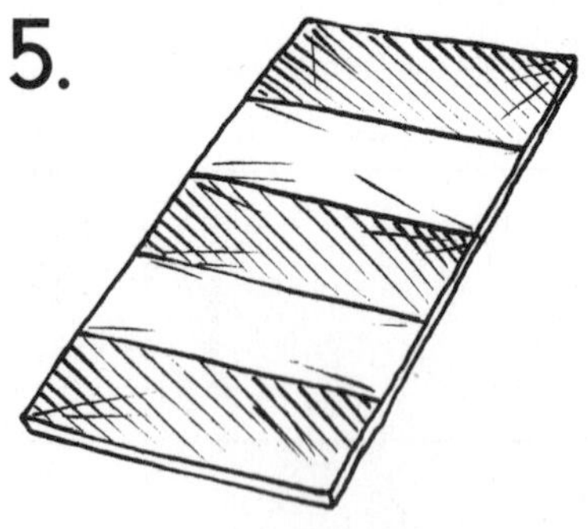

See the ____.

6. 

See the ____.

Name ______________________ Date ________

Sounds and Spellings

Directions: Practice writing *i* and *I*. Copy the words. Then, write the words that have the /i/ sound.

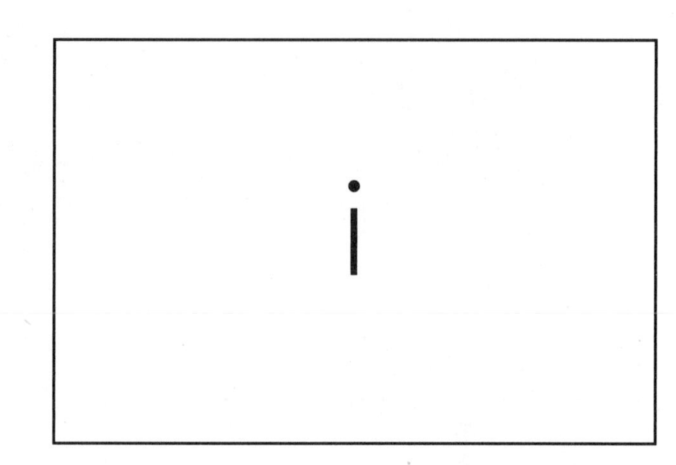

Practice A

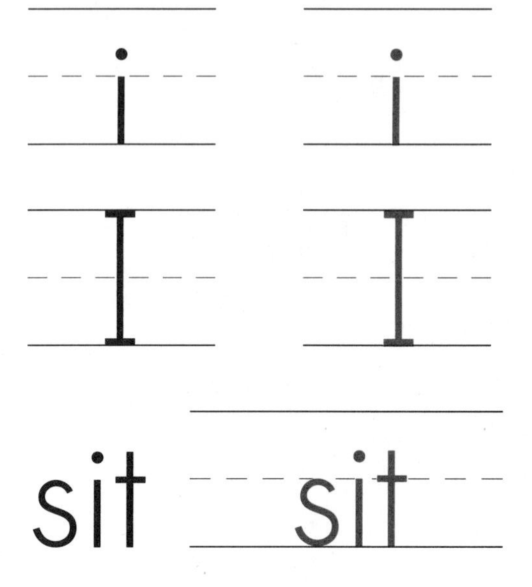

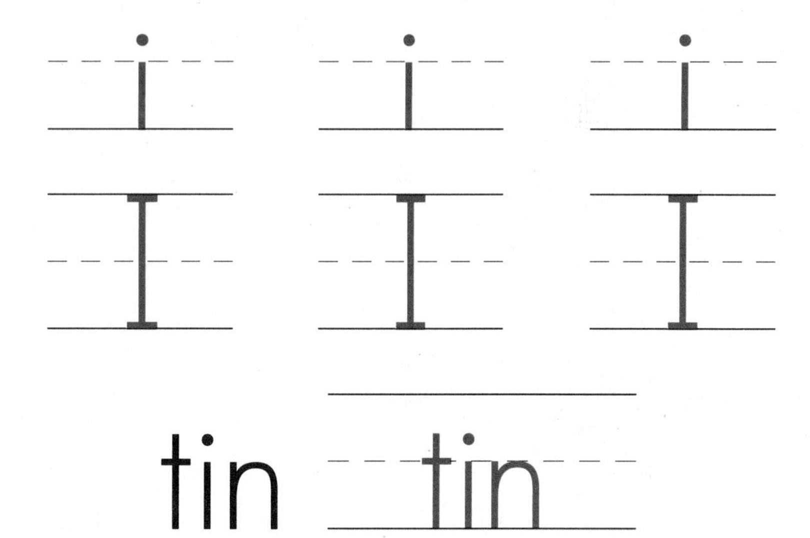

sit sit tin tin

Practice B

Directions: Form words by saying the sounds and writing the letters represented by each **Sound/Spelling Card** picture.

Name ______________________ Date ________

Nouns

Practice A

Directions: Name each picture and tell whether it is a person, place, or thing. Write it on the line.

1\.

person

2\.

thing

3\.

place

4\.

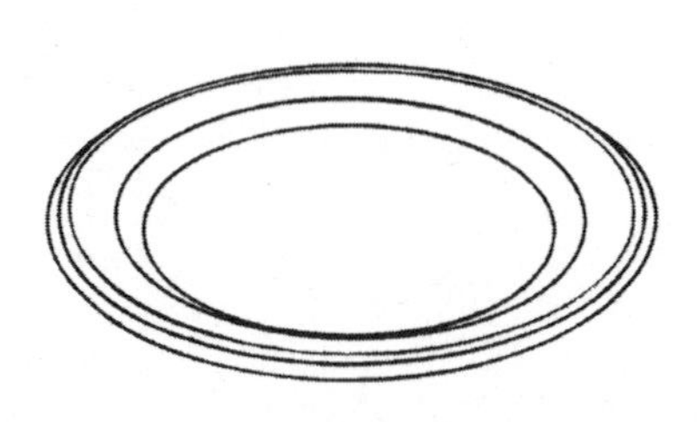

thing

5\.

place

6\.

person

Practice B

Directions: Listen as your teacher reads each sentence. Underline the noun in each one.

7. There is a bat.

8. There is a mat.

9. Sam sees.

10. A mast is there.

11. It is a mitt.

12. Dad sits.

Name ______________________ **Date** ________

Directions: Practice writing *h* and *H*. Then draw two pictures whose names begin with the /h/ sound.

Sounds and Spellings

h

Practice A

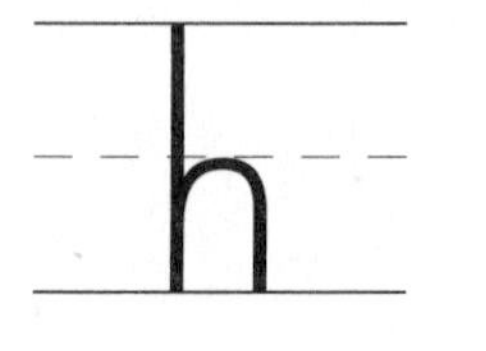 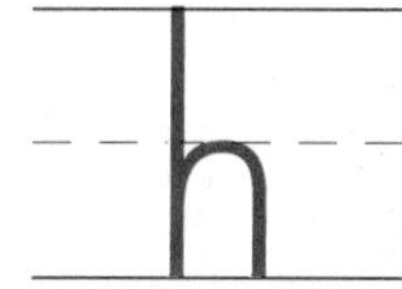 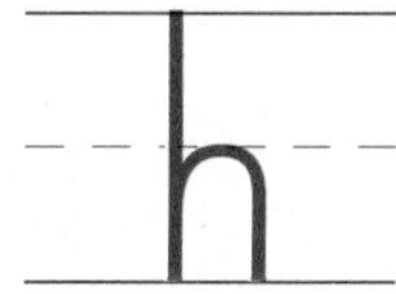 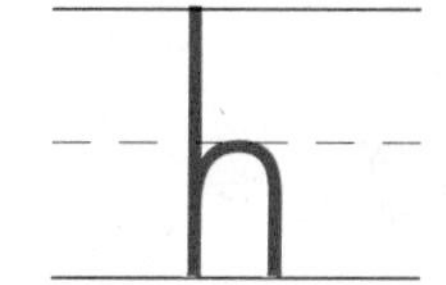 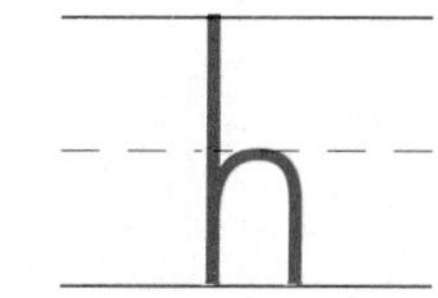

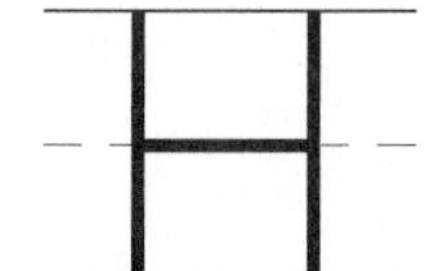 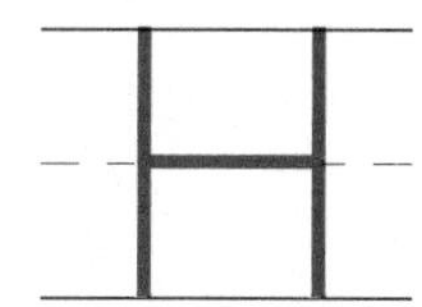 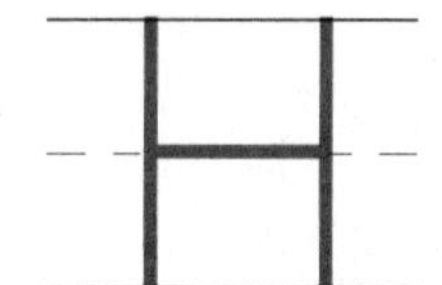 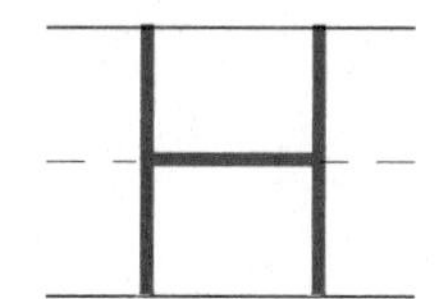 H

1. Answers will vary. Picture must begin with the /h/ sound.

2. Answers will vary. Picture must begin with the /h/ sound.

Practice B

Directions: Say the name of each picture. Write a capital *H* on the line if the picture begins with the /h/ sound.

3. 

H

4. 

H

5. 

6. 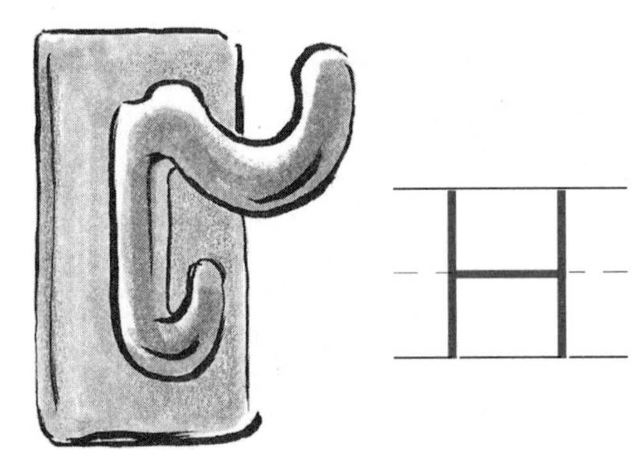

H

7. 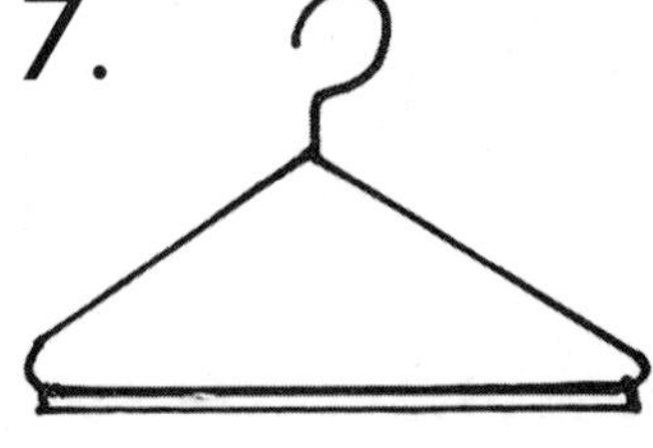

H

8. 

H

Name ________________________________ Date ________

Sounds and Spellings

Practice A

Directions: Say the name of each picture. Write the spelling for the sound you hear at the beginning of each word.

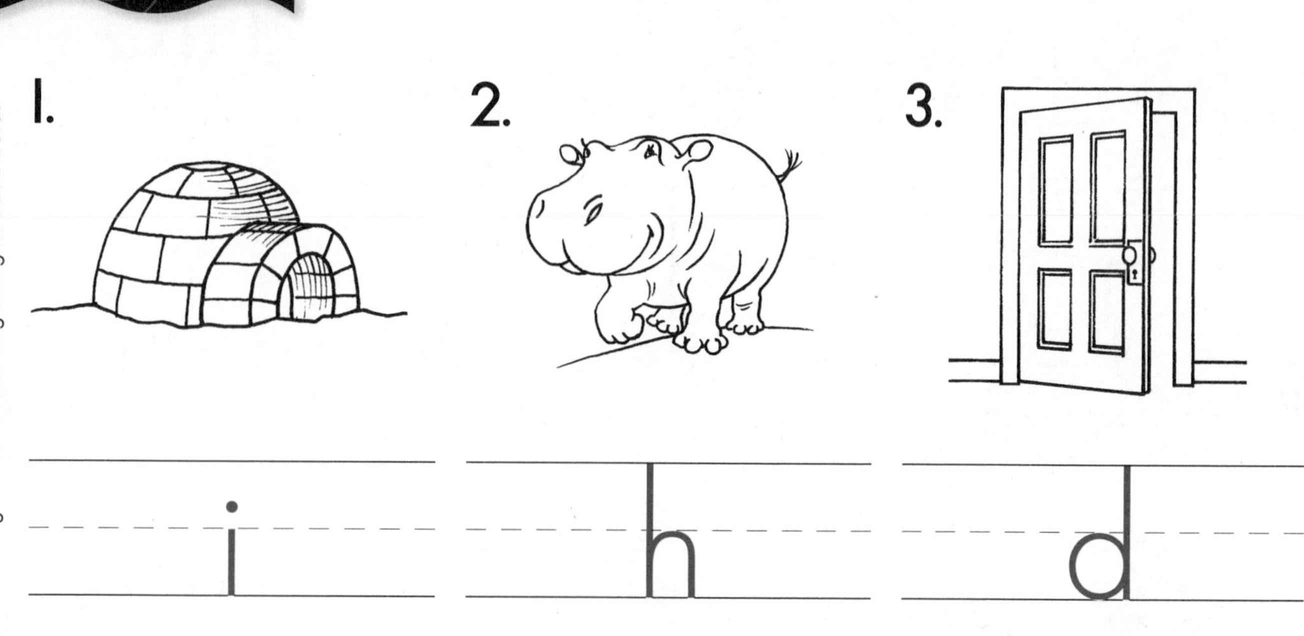

Practice B

Directions: Play Riddle Me This! Say the sound for each card. Write the spelling for each sound. Then say the sound for each one. Blend them together to make a word. Write the word on the line.

7.

hid

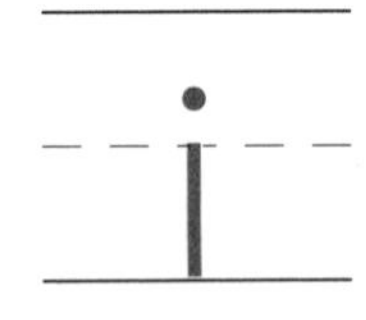
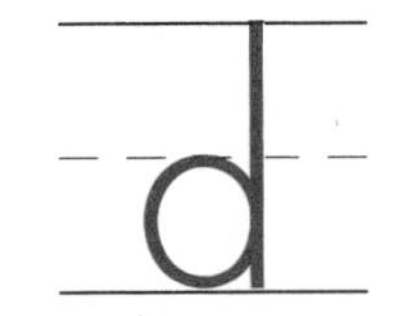

h i d

8.

hint

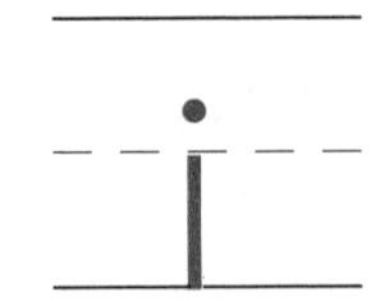
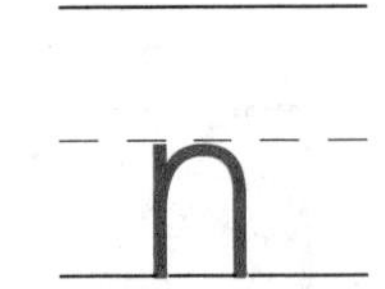
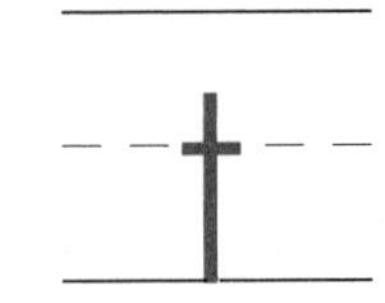

h i n t

9.

hand

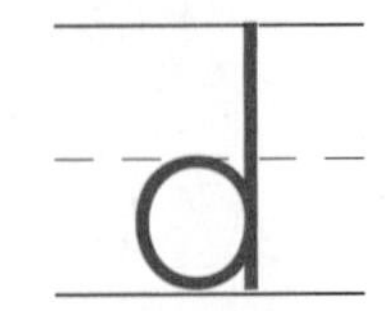

h a n d

Name ________________________ Date ________

Directions: Practice writing *p* and *P*. Copy the words.

Sounds and Spellings

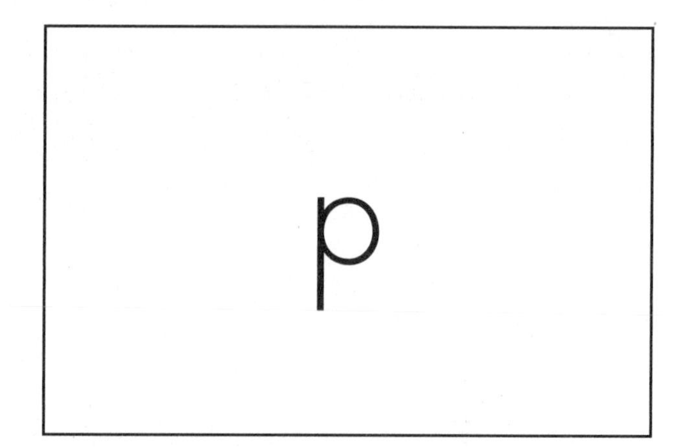

Practice A

p p p p p

P P P P P

pat pat hip hip

Practice B

Directions: Circle the sentence that matches the picture. Write the correct sentence for the last picture.

1. Pam is on a pan.
   Pam is on a mat.

2. I tap the map.
   I pat the hat.

3. Pat naps.
   Pat is on the sand.

4. Pat naps.

Name ______________________ Date ________

Sounds and Spellings

Directions: Practice writing l and L. Then, draw two pictures whose names have the /l/ sound.

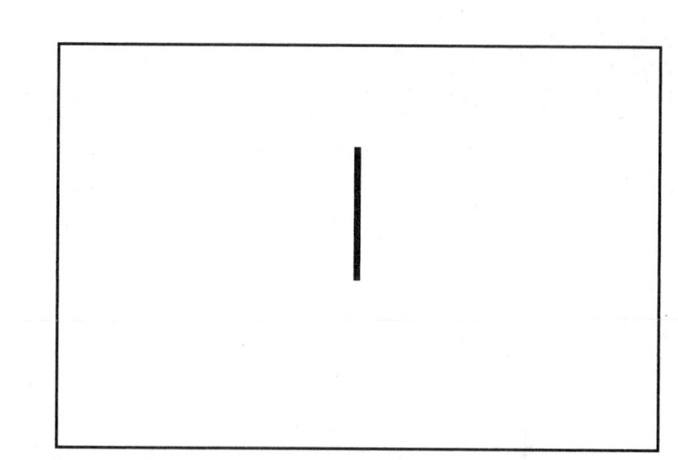

Practice A

l l l l l

L L L L L

1. Answers will vary. Picture must begin with the /l/ sound.

2. Answers will vary. Picture must begin with the /l/ sound.

Practice B

Directions: Draw a line from each word to the picture that goes with it.

3. list

4. lamp

5. hill

6. pals

7. lips

Name ______________________ Date ________

Directions: Practice writing o and O. Copy the words.

Sounds and Spellings

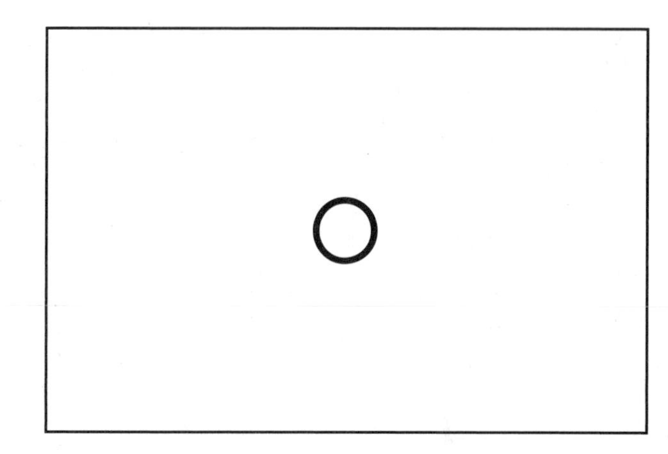

Practice A

o o o o o

O O O O O

not not stop stop

Practice B

Directions: Look at the pictures and read the sentences. Circle the correct word to complete each sentence.

1. 

Tom has a ____.

pat
pot

2. 

Sam can ____.

hop
hip

3. 

It is a ________.

map
mop

Name ______________________ **Date** ________

Singular and Plural Nouns

Practice A

Directions: Listen as your teacher reads each word next to its picture. Draw a line from each word to its plural.

1. Welcome mat — homes

2.  boy — mitts

3.  home — mats

4.  dog — boys

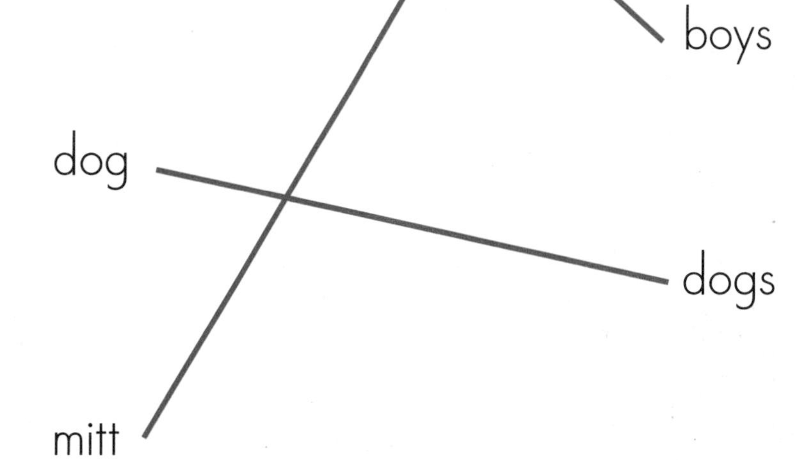

5.  mitt — dogs

Practice B

Directions: Look at each picture, and listen as your teacher reads the words. Write each word to make it show more than one.

6.  hat — hats

7.  ball — balls

8.  bird — birds

9. 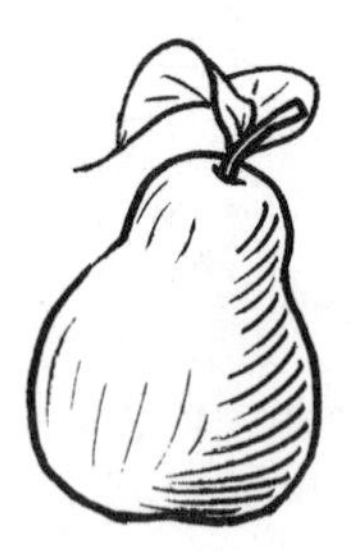 pear — pears

10.  girl — girls

Name ________________________ Date ________

Sounds and Spellings

Directions: Practice writing *b* and *B*. Then, draw two pictures whose names have the /b/ sound.

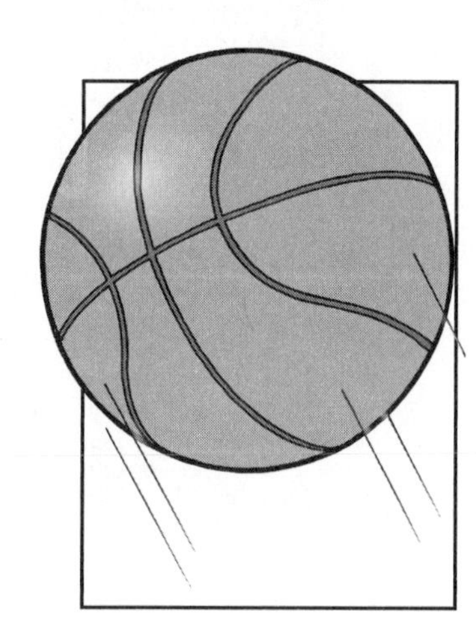

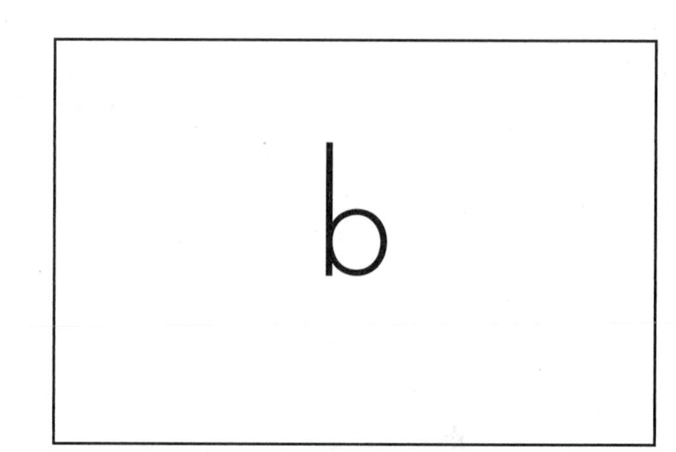

Practice A

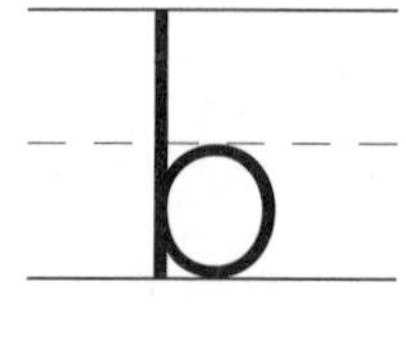 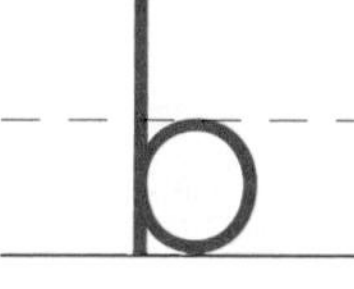 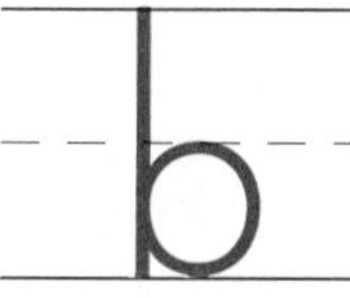 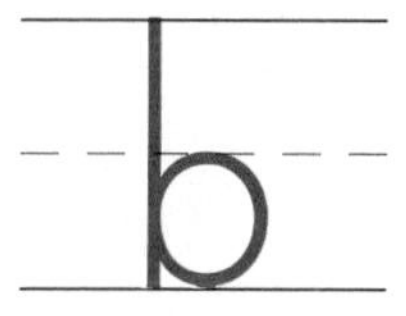 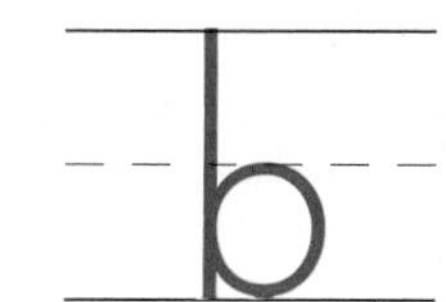

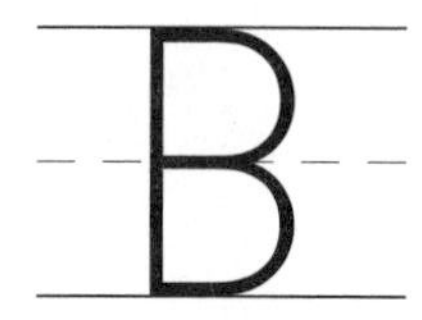 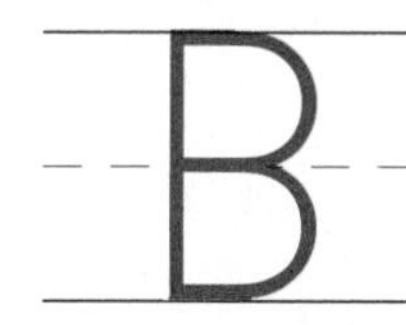 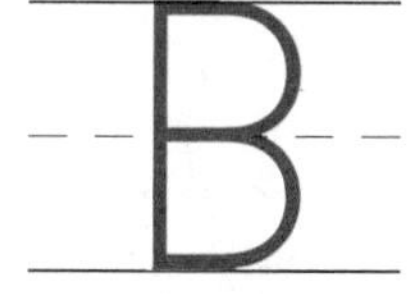 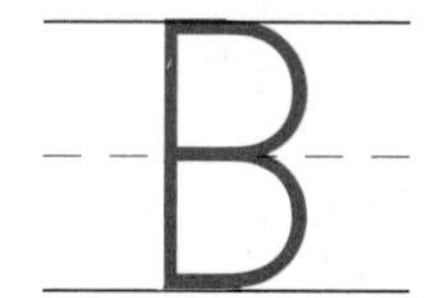

1. Answers will vary. Picture must begin with the /b/ sound.

2. Answers will vary. Picture must begin with the /b/ sound.

Practice B

Directions: Circle the word or sentence that matches each picture. Then, write the sentence you circled.

3.

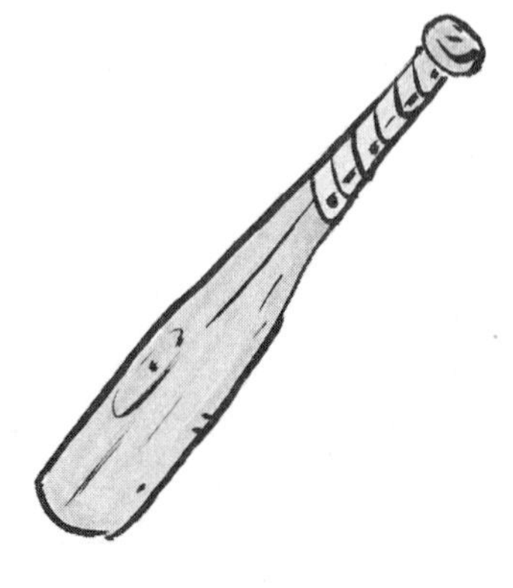

bin

4.

bob

5.

Nan has a bat.

Nan has a bib.

6. Nan has a bat.

Name ______________________ Date ________

Review Sounds and Spellings

Directions: Read the words in the box. Write each word under the correct picture.

list	stamp	pond	Matt	hill	bat

1.

pond

2.

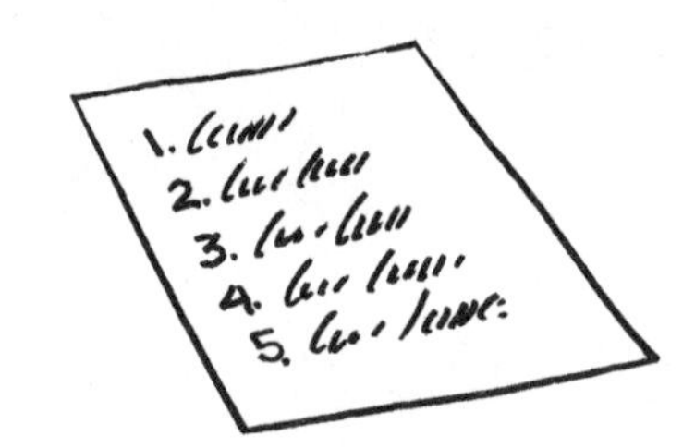

list

3.

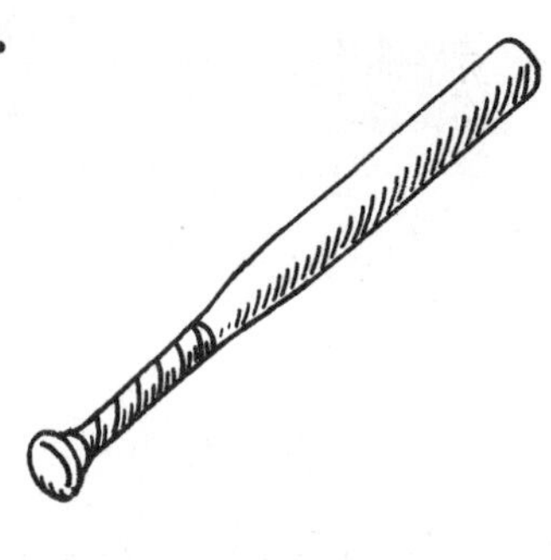

bat

4.

stamp

5.

hill

6.

Matt

Practice B

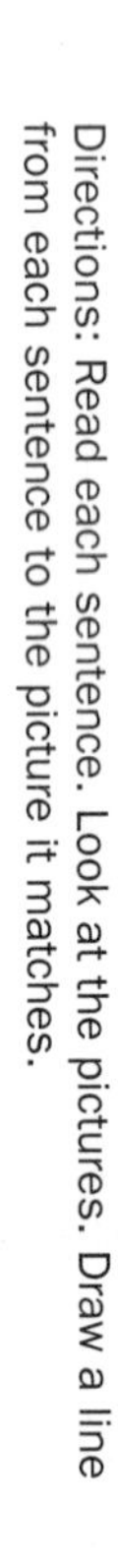
Directions: Read each sentence. Look at the pictures. Draw a line from each sentence to the picture it matches.

7. Tom has a mop.

8. Todd did a handstand on the hill.

9. Ann is in the band.

10. Mom hid mints in the tan pot.

Directions: Practice writing c and C. Copy the words. Then, draw two pictures whose names begin with the /k/ sound.

Name ______________________ Date ________

Sounds and Spellings

c

Practice A

c c c c c

C C C C C

can can

call call

1. Answers will vary. Picture must begin with the /k/ sound.

2. Answers will vary. Picture must begin with the /k/ sound.

Practice B

can	cot	ball	cab

Directions: Write the correct word under each picture. Then, circle the correct word to finish the sentence and write the word on the line.

3. 

cab

4. 

can

5. 

ball

6. 

cot

7. 

Dan has a  cat.

cot

cat

Name ______________________________ Date __________

Sounds and Spellings

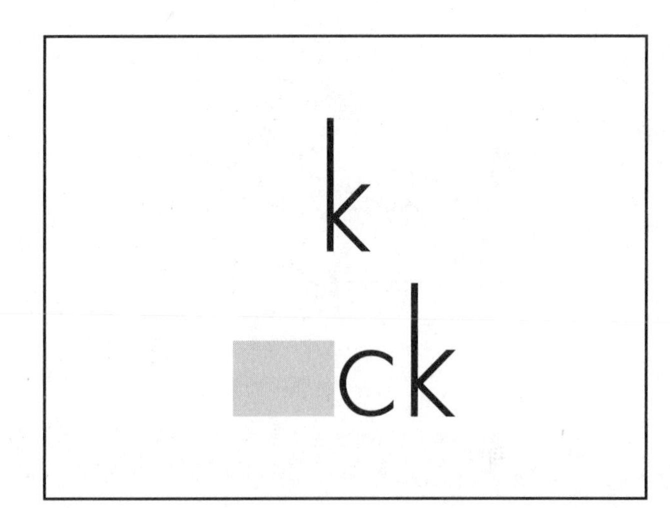

Practice A

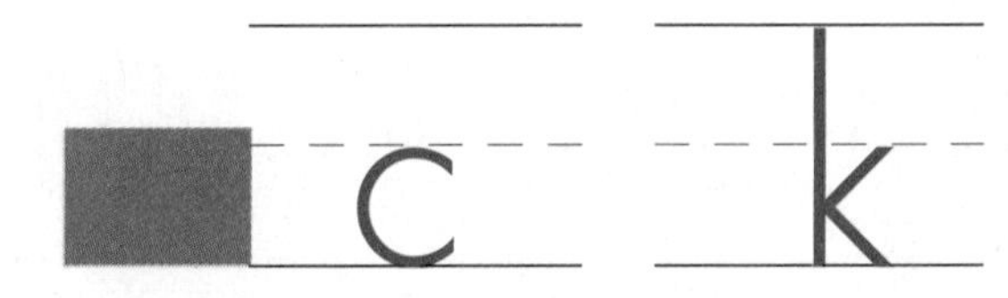

1. clo c k
2. k it
3. so c k

Directions: At the top, color the box green, write the letters for the spelling, and say the /k/ sound. At the bottom, finish the words by writing *k* or *ck* in the blanks. Read each word. Then draw a line from the word to the picture it matches.

Practice B

Directions: Circle the sentence that describes the picture.

4. Kim packs the socks.

Kim stacks the sacks.

5. Nick sits in the back.

Nick sits on the dock.

6. Skip has a backpack.

Skip sits on a stack of sacks.

Directions: Practice writing *r* and *R*. Copy the words. Then, draw two pictures whose names begin with the /r/ sound.

Name ______________________ **Date** __________

Sounds and Spellings

r

Practice A

r r r r r

R R R R R

rat rat

rack rack

1. Answers will vary. Picture must begin with the /r/ sound.

2. Answers will vary. Picture must begin with the /r/ sound.

Practice B

Directions: Circle the sentence that describes the picture. Write the sentence for the last picture.

3.

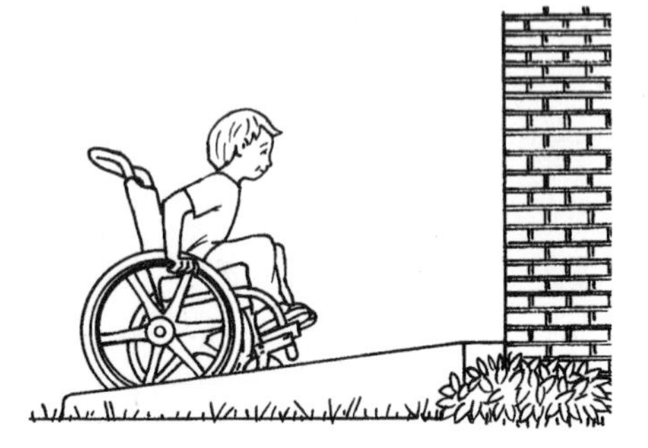

Ron ran on the rocks.

Rick is on the ramp.

4.

The rat sat on a rock.

The ram ran up the ramp.

5.

Ron rips the sack.

A rabbit hops.

6. A rabbit hops.

Name ____________________ Date __________

Adjectives

Focus

Rule Describing words tell more about something.

Example It is a *sunny* day.

Practice A

Directions: Write the word that describes each picture.

small	hot	pretty	tall

1. small

2. pretty

3. hot

4. tall

Practice B

Directions: Look at the picture. Write an adjective from the box that describes the animal. The first one is done for you.

small	spotted	muddy	sleepy

5. muddy

6. small

7. sleepy

8. spotted

Directions: Trace the spellings. Then write them in the blanks as you say the sounds. At the bottom, write the word that names each picture.

Name ______________________ Date ________

Sounds and Spellings

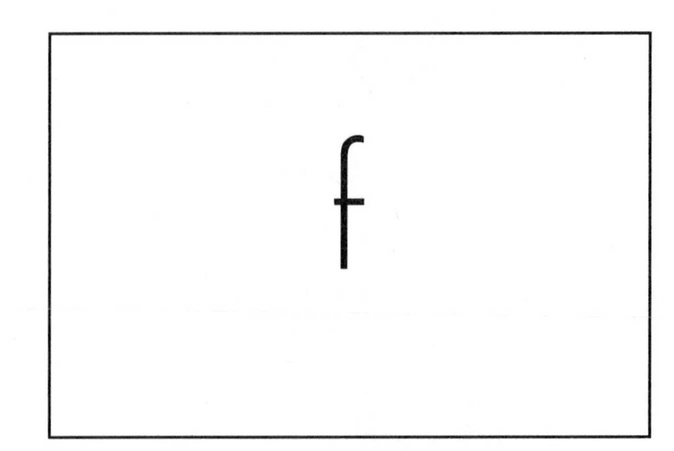

Practice A

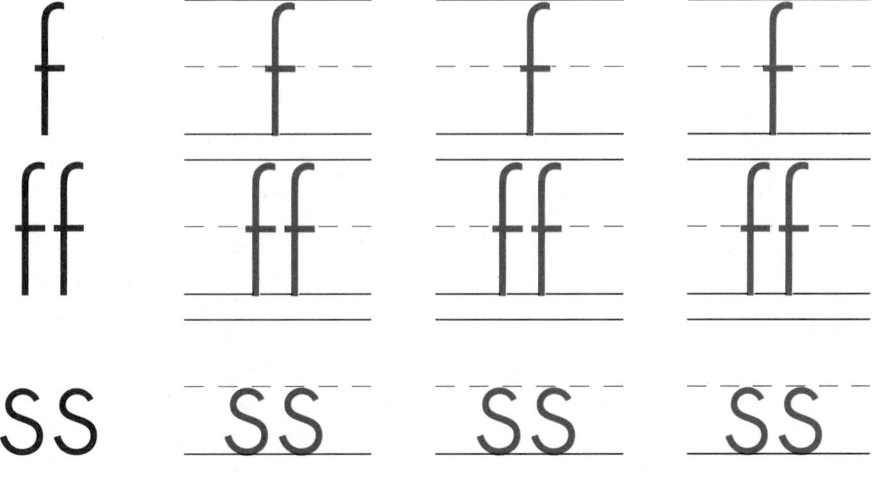

miss
sniff

1. 

miss

2. 

sniff

Practice B

Directions: Circle the word that names each picture.

3.

cliff stiff

4.

kick kiss

5.

hiss kiss

6.

fast fist

Name ______________________ Date ________

Sounds and Spellings

Practice A

Directions: Look at the pictures. Circle the correct word to finish each sentence. Write the correct word for the last one.

1.

Bob has a ________.

sock
sack

2.

Nan tips the ________.

rock
cup

3.

Ron has a .

rock
tack

UNIT 2 Lesson 5

Practice B

Directions: Read the words in the box and name the pictures. Then, write the word that goes with each picture.

fan	cat	ramp	cut

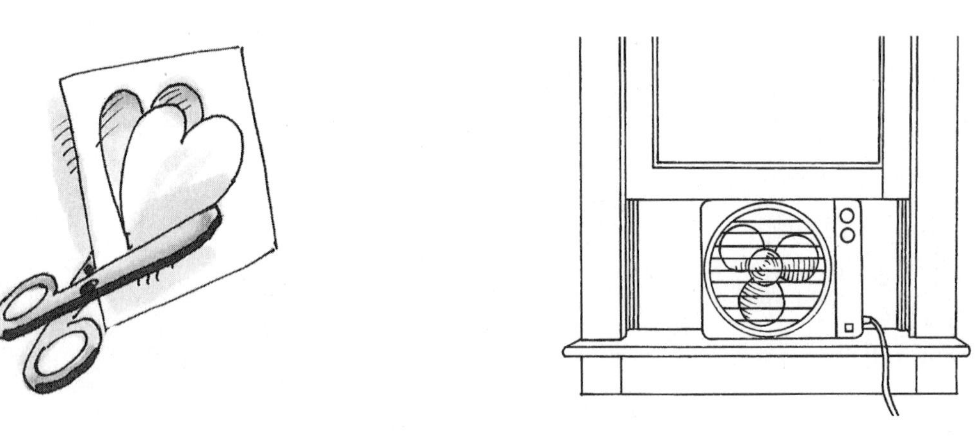

cut fan

ramp cat

Name ______________________ Date ________

Directions: Practice writing *g* and G. Copy the words. Then, draw two pictures whose names contain the /g/ sound.

Sounds and Spellings

g

Practice A

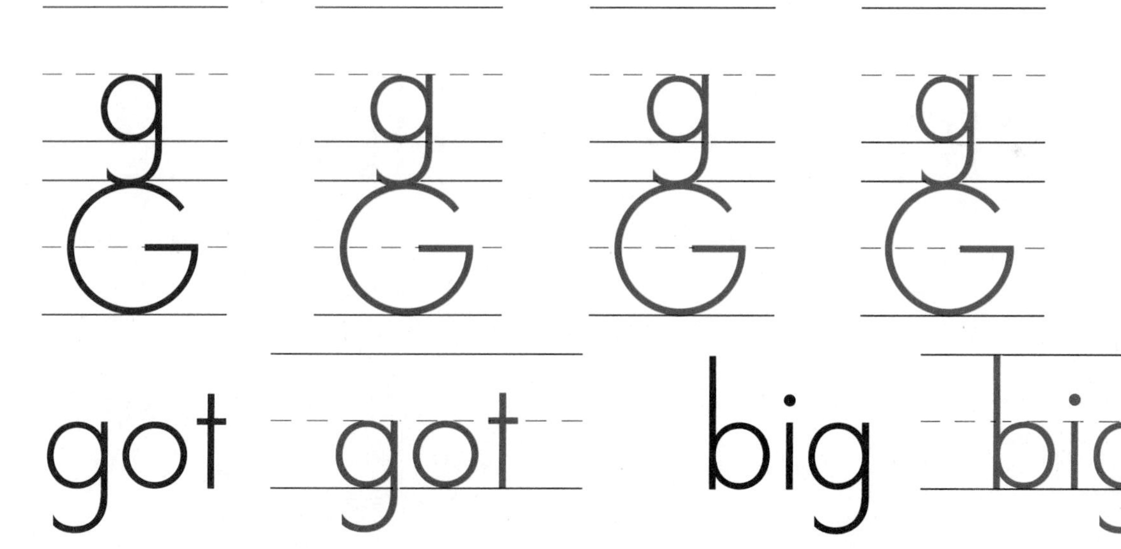

1. Answers will vary. Picture must contain the /g/ sound.

2. Answers will vary. Picture must contain the /g/ sound.

Practice B

Directions: Circle the two words that tell about each picture. At the bottom, write the two words you circled for the last picture.

3.

bag big dog

4.

pig dig log

5. pig

6. log

Directions: Practice writing *j* and *J*. Copy the words. Then, draw two pictures whose names have the /j/ sound.

Name ________________ **Date** ________

Sounds and Spellings

Practice A

1. Answers will vary. Picture must contain the /j/ sound.

2. Answers will vary. Picture must contain the /j/ sound.

Practice B

Directions: Read the two sentences, circle the sentence that describes the picture, and write the sentence on the line. Say the name of each picture to the student. Then, have the student write the name of each picture and underline the /j/ spelling.

3.

There was a traffic jam.

Jan can jog on the ramp.

There was a traffic jam.

4.

bridge

5.

badge

Directions: Practice writing *u* and *U*. Copy the words. Then, draw two pictures whose names have the /u/ sound.

Name ______________________ Date ________

Sounds and Spellings

u

Practice A

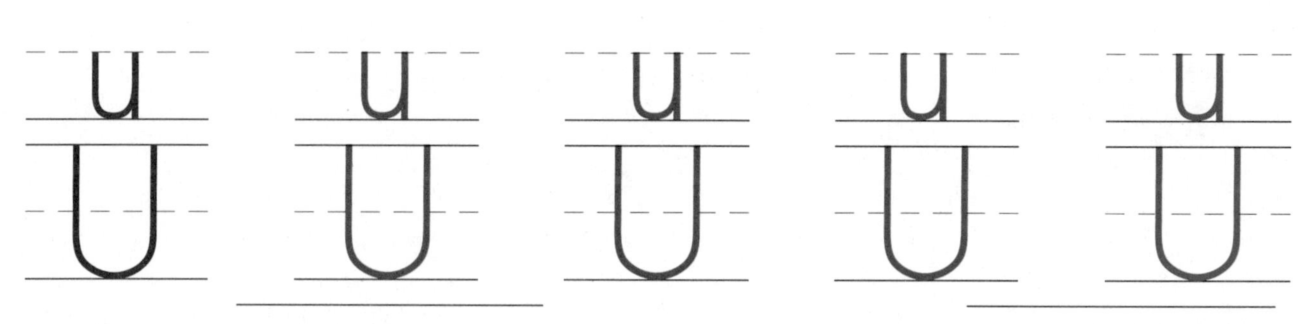

run run must must

1. Answers will vary. Picture must contain the /u/ sound.

2. Answers will vary. Picture must contain the /u/ sound.

Practice B

Directions: Circle the sentence that describes each picture. Write the last sentence on the line.

3.

Bud is stuck in the mud.

Bud picks up the pup.

4.

A sub is in the tub.

Mud is on the duck.

5.

Pam picks up a cup.

Pam runs to the bus.

6. Pam runs to the bus.

Name ______________________ Date ________

Possessive Nouns

Focus

Rule Add 's to a noun to show who owns or has something.

Examples Tom's mitt Nico's pants

Practice A

Directions: Read each noun phrase. Then draw a line from the phrase to the picture it matches. Trace the apostrophes with a red crayon.

1. Bob's bat
2. cat's hiss
3. Rick's glass
4. pig's grunt

5. Dad's clock

Practice B

Directions: Read each sentence. Circle the word that completes each one and write it on the blank. At the bottom, read each phrase and draw a picture to match it.

6. The cap's brim is stiff.

cap's cat's

7. The bug's rug is snug.

bag's bug's

8. Fran's hat is black.

Fran's Fan's

9. Answers will vary, but picture should match the words below the box.

Sam's badge

10. Answers will vary, but picture should match the words below the box.

Mom's bag

Name ______________________ Date ________

Sounds and Spellings

Directions: Practice writing /z/ spellings as you say the sound. At the bottom of the page, read and copy the words. Circle the spelling for /z/ in each word.

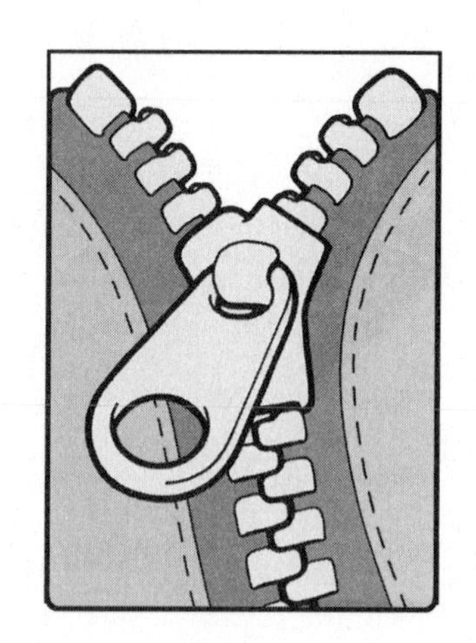

z

_s

Practice A

z z z z z

zz zz zz zz

_s s s s

1. zip zip 2. his his

UNIT 2 Lesson 9

Practice B

Directions: Write the name of each picture and underline the /z/ spelling. At the bottom of the page, read each word. Draw a picture to match each one.

3.

bee

4.

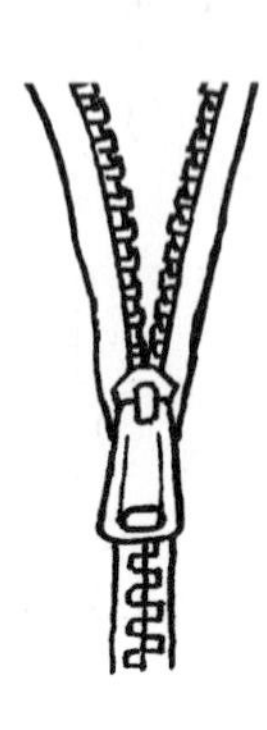

zip

5.

fuzz

6. Drawing should be of a zigzag.

zigzag

7. Drawing should be of pins.

pins

8. Drawing should be of hills.

hills

Name ______________________ **Date** ________

Sounds and Spellings Review

Practice A

Directions: Look at each picture. Circle the word to finish each sentence.

I.

The judge's hand was up.

judge's
crab's

2.

The cub had  on his fuzz.

jug
jam

3.

Jan has a big .

crab
cab

Practice B

Directions: Read the words in the box. Look at the pictures. Choose the word from the box that names each picture and write the word underneath it.

drums	judge	fizz	zigzag

4.

drums

5.

zigzag

6.

judge

7.

fizz

Directions: Practice writing x and X. Copy the word. Then, draw two pictures whose names end with the /ks/ sound.

Name ______________________ Date ________

Sounds and Spellings

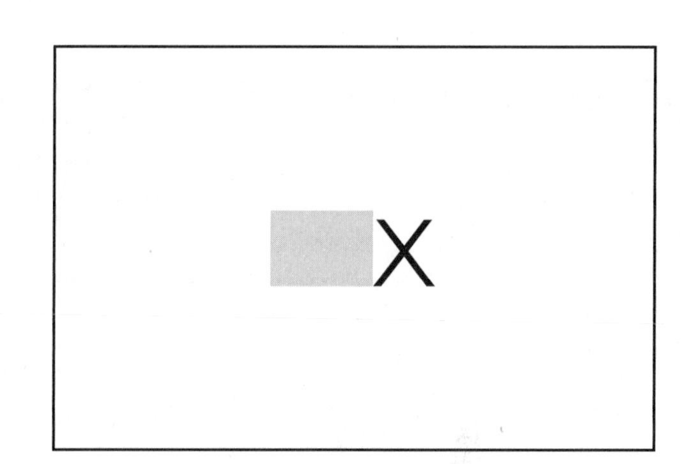

Practice A

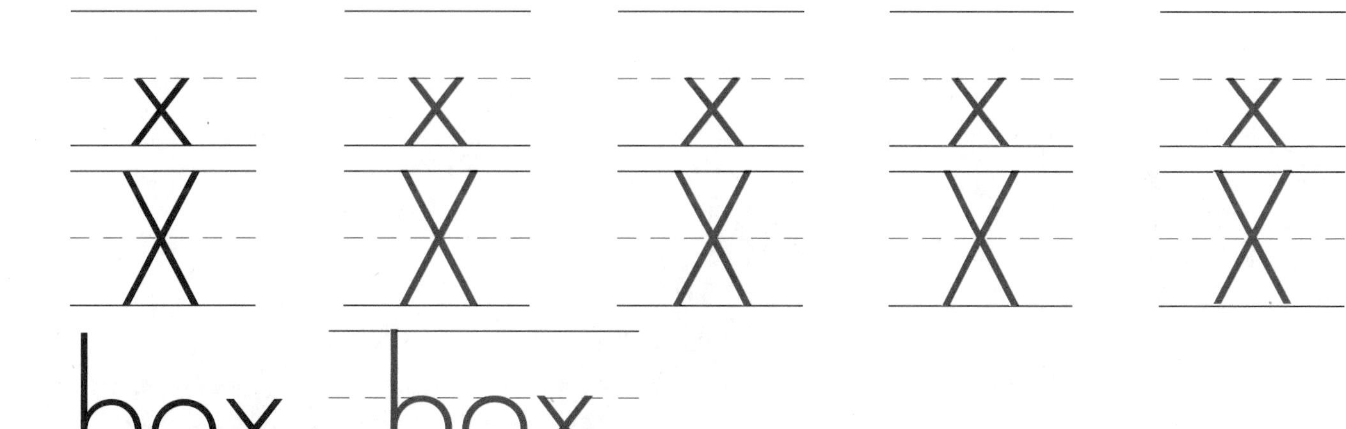

box box

1. Answers will vary. Picture must end with the /ks/ sound.

2. Answers will vary. Picture must end with the /ks/ sound.

Practice B

Directions: Circle the correct word for the picture. On the bottom, write *a*, *i*, or o on the line to correctly complete each word.

3.

pod pad

4.

ox ax

5.

mitt mutt

6.

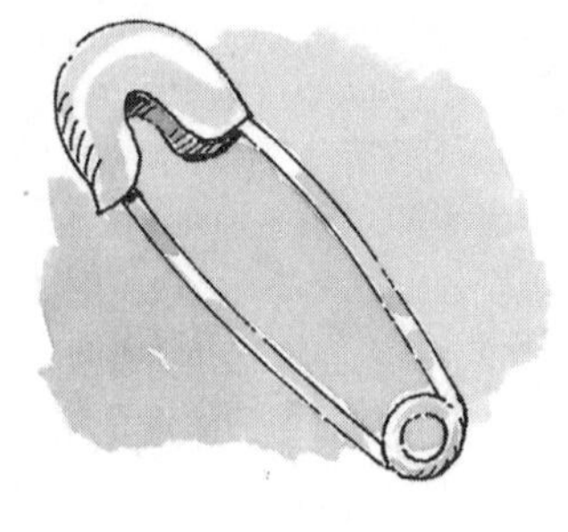

p_i_n

7.

b_a_t

8.

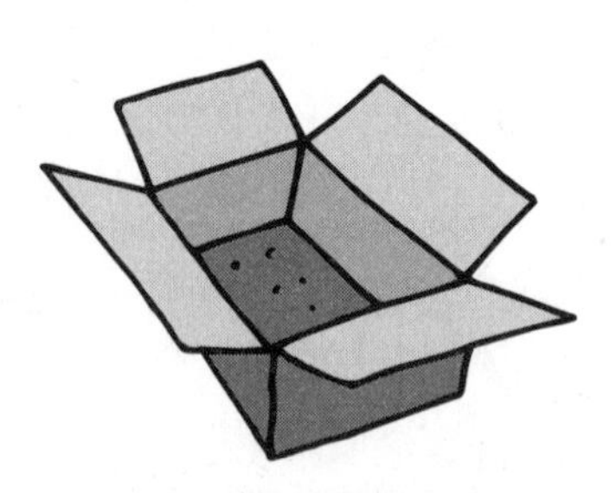

b_o_x

Directions: Practice writing e and *E*. Copy the words. Then, draw two pictures whose names have the /e/ sound.

Name ______________________ Date ________

Sounds and Spellings

e

Practice A

e e e e e

E E E E E

pet pet red red

1. Answers will vary. Picture must contain the /e/ sound.

2. Answers will vary. Picture must contain the /e/ sound.

Practice B

Directions: Write the correct word beside each picture. Then, write the letters for the sounds represented by the ***Sound/Spelling Card*** pictures. Finally, read the sentence and write the missing word.

pet	tent	bed	neck

3. 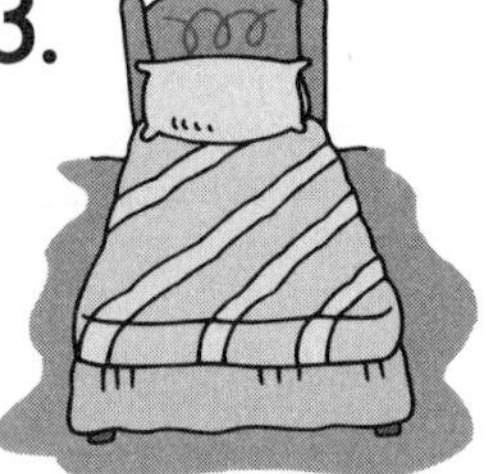 bed

4.  pet

5.  tent

6.  neck

7. 

 t e n

8. Ted has ten pens.

UNIT 2 Lesson 13

Name ______________________ Date ________

Sounds and Spellings

Practice A

Directions: Write each word and add *ed* to the end. Read the words and listen to the ending sound.

1. melt melted
2. miss missed
3. buzz buzzed
4. trick tricked
5. call called
6. plant planted

Practice B

Directions: Add *ed* to each word and write it in the blank to complete each sentence. Read the sentences.

7. I handed Mom a gift.
hand

8. The cat hissed at Jack.
hiss

9. The pig jumped in the mud.
jump

10. The hot sun melted the snack.
melt

UNIT 2 Lesson 13

Name ______________________ Date ________

Verbs

Focus

Rule Verbs are action words. They tell you what a person or thing does.

Practice A

Directions: Read each sentence. Circle the action verb. Connect the sentence to the picture it matches.

1. Lin hits the ball.
2. Dan slipped on the hill.
3. Bob sat on Fran's hat.
4. Jack jumps on the bed.
5. Pat's cat hissed at red ants.

Helping Verbs

Focus **Rule** Helping verbs help action verbs to show when the action happens.

Directions: Read each sentence. Underline the helping verb and circle the action verb in each one.

Practice B

1. The cats have hissed at the ball.
2. Fran had called Dad at the mall.
3. Stan was helped up the steps.
4. Max has snapped the twig on a rock.
5. Rob had jumped on Mom's bed.

Directions: Practice writing the /e/ spellings as you say the sound. At the bottom of the page, write *ea* in the blanks to finish each word. Read the words. Then, draw a line from the word to the matching picture.

Name ______________________ Date ________

Sounds and Spellings

e

_ea_

Practice A

e   e e e e

_ea_   _ea_ _ea_

_ea_ _ea_

1. Picture of a head.

h ea d

2. Picture of bread.

br ea d

Practice B

Directions: Read the sentences. Circle the best word to complete each one. Write the word in the blank.

3. Spread red jam on the bread.
dread (bread)

4. He meant to go to the west end of the deck.
(meant) tent

5. Mom read to Max and Jen.
red (read)

6. The map lead us to the picnic spot.
(lead) lad

Name ______________________ Date ________

Sounds and Spellings Review

Practice A

Directions: Draw a line to connect the two words that go together. Write the compound words on the lines. At the bottom, draw a picture for each word.

sand	pen
pig	stand
head	box

1. sandbox
2. pigpen
3. headstand

4. Picture of a person doing a headstand.

headstand

5. Picture of a pigpen.

pigpen

Practice B

Directions: Read each sentence. Circle the best word to complete each one. Write the word on the line.

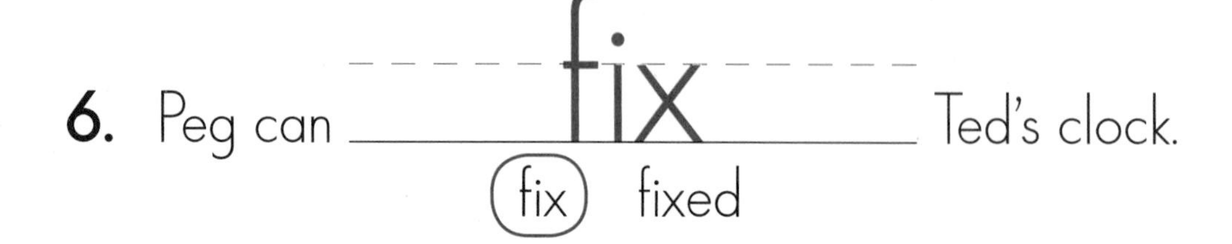

6. Peg can fix Ted's clock.
   (fix) fixed

7. Tom had a snack and rested.
   rest (rested)

8. Pam grabbed the ball and kicked it.
   grab (grabbed)

9. Fred sat on the bed and hissed.
   hiss (hissed)

10. Jill and Jen had bread and jam.
    bed (bread)

Name ______________________ Date ________

Sounds and Spellings

Directions: Practice writing *sh* and *Sh*. Then, draw two pictures whose names begin with the /sh/ sound.

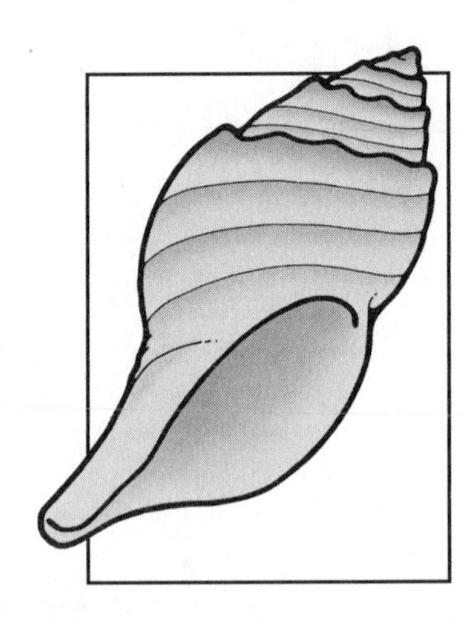

sh

Practice A

sh sh sh sh sh

Sh Sh Sh Sh Sh

1. Answers will vary. Picture must begin with the /sh/ sound.

2. Answers will vary. Picture must begin with the /sh/ sound.

Practice B

Directions: Write the correct word under each picture. At the bottom, write the letters represented by each ***Sound/Spelling Card*** to form a word.

shop	shed	shut	fish

3. shut

4. shed

5. fish

6. shop

7. sh i f t

Name ______________________ Date ________

Directions: Practice writing *th* and *Th*. Then, draw two pictures whose names begin with the /th/ sound.

Sounds and Spellings

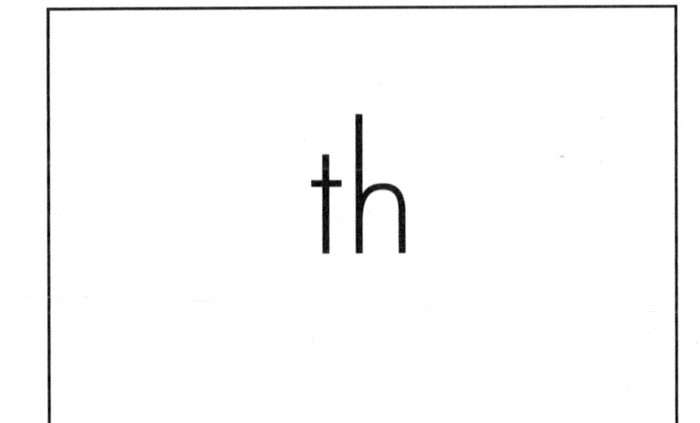

Practice A

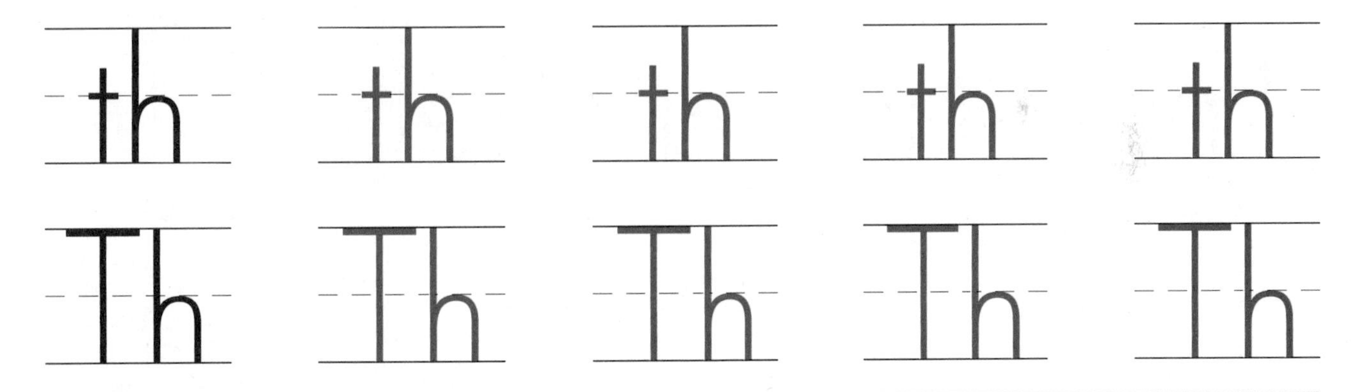

1. Answers will vary. Picture must begin with the /th/ sound.

2. Answers will vary. Picture must begin with the /th/ sound.

Practice B

Directions: Unscramble the words to make a sentence. Write the sentence. Say the name of each picture to the student. Have the student write the name of each picture and underline the /th/ spelling.

shell.	Thad	a	has

Thad has a shell.

4.

thin

5.

bath

6.

path

Name ______________________ **Date** ________

Directions: Practice writing *ch* and *tch*. Copy the words.

Sounds and Spellings

ch

tch

Practice A

ch ch ch ch ch

tch tch tch tch tch

chip chip itch itch

Practice B

Directions: Say the name of each picture to the student. Have the student write the name of the picture and underline the /ch/ spelling.

hatch	chip	pitch

1. chip
2. pitch
3. hatch
4. chop
5. match
6. chin

Name ______________________ Date ________

Sentences and Capital Letters

Focus

Rule Sentences start with **capital letters**.

Practice A

Directions: Draw a line under the first letter in each sentence. Read the sentences. Draw a line to connect each sentence with its picture.

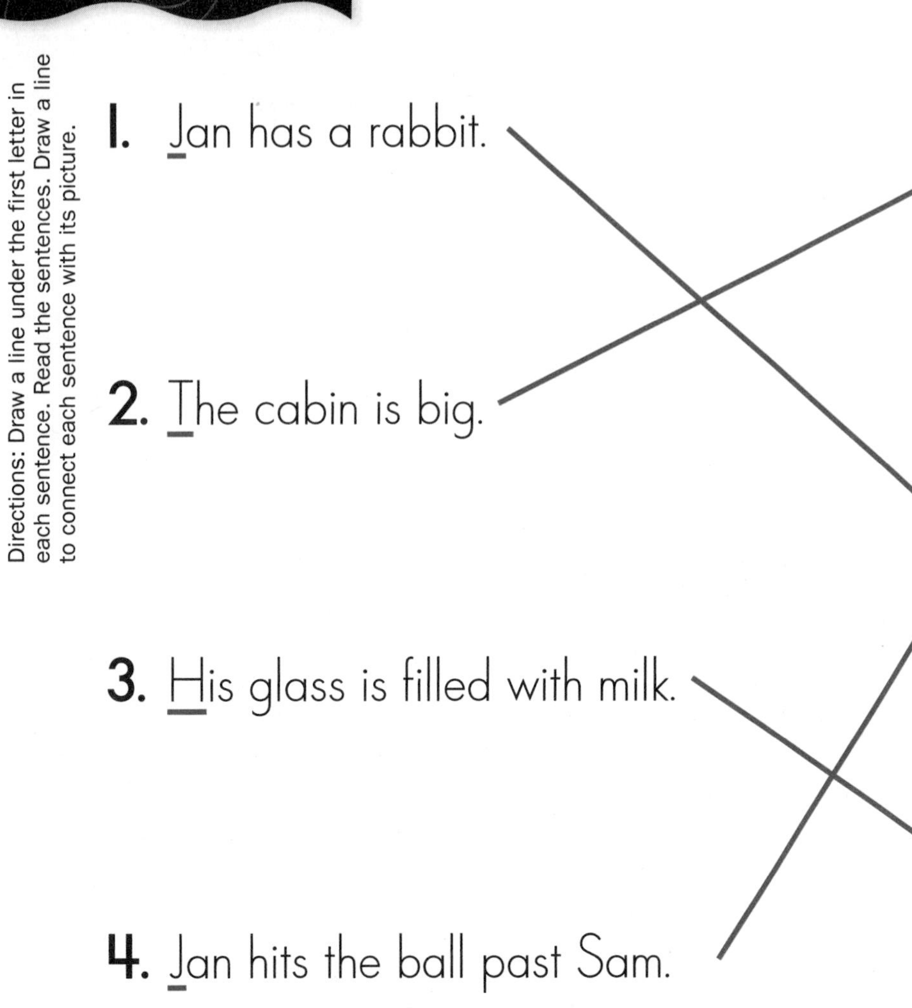

1. Jan has a rabbit.
2. The cabin is big.
3. His glass is filled with milk.
4. Jan hits the ball past Sam.

Practice B

Directions: Circle the incorrect letter. Copy each sentence correctly on the line.

1. the top spins.

The top spins.

2. beth snacks on plums.

Beth snacks on plums.

3. mom went to the mall.

Mom went to the mall.

4. rob fixed Tim's truck.

Rob fixed Tim's truck.

Directions: Trace the spellings. On the blank lines, write the word from the box that goes with each picture.

Name ______________________ **Date** ________

Sounds and Spellings

or

ore

Practice A

store **fork** **horn**

1. 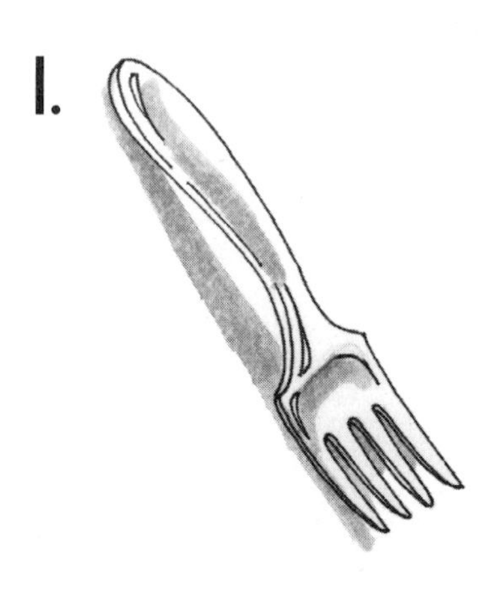
2. 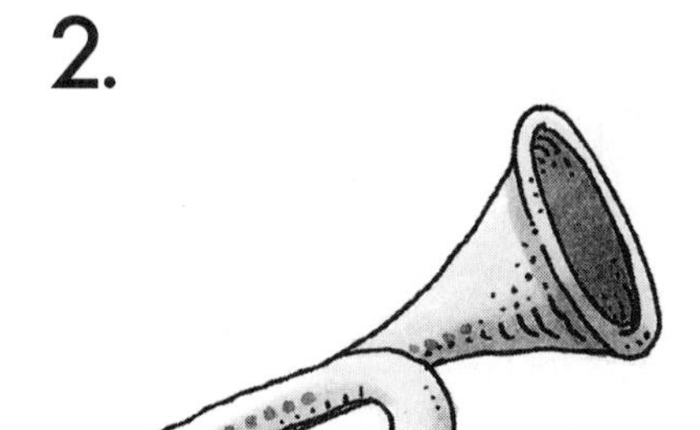
3. 

Practice B

Directions: Write the spellings on the lines to finish the words. Read the rhyming words. Then, read the sentence. Circle the words that rhyme.

or	ore	or
c o r k	m o r e	b o r n
f o r k	sc o r e	c o r n
st o r k	w o r e	th o r n

The stork got the pork with his fork.

Name ______________________ Date ________

Sounds and Spellings Review

Practice A

Directions: On the blank lines, write the word from the box that goes with each picture.

core	match	thread
chin	shed	corn

shed

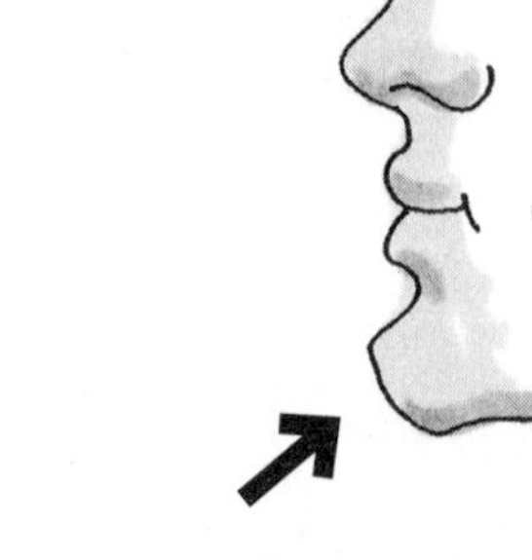

chin

match

corn

thread

core

Practice B

Directions: Read each sentence. Circle the word that completes the sentence.

1. The ________ was the sixth man to bat.

2. Chuck the ________ can catch a ball.

champs chimp

4. She will ________ the thick shrubs.

3. The bad ________ smashed the shed and bench.

Name ______________________ **Date** ________

Sounds and Spellings

Directions: Practice writing *ar*. Copy the words. Then, draw two pictures whose names have the /ar/ sound.

ar

Practice A

ar ar ar ar ar

art art cart cart

1. Answers will vary. Picture must contain the /ar/ sound.

2. Answers will vary. Picture must contain the /ar/ sound.

Practice B

Directions: Circle the pictures whose names have the /ar/ sound. Write each word under the correct picture.

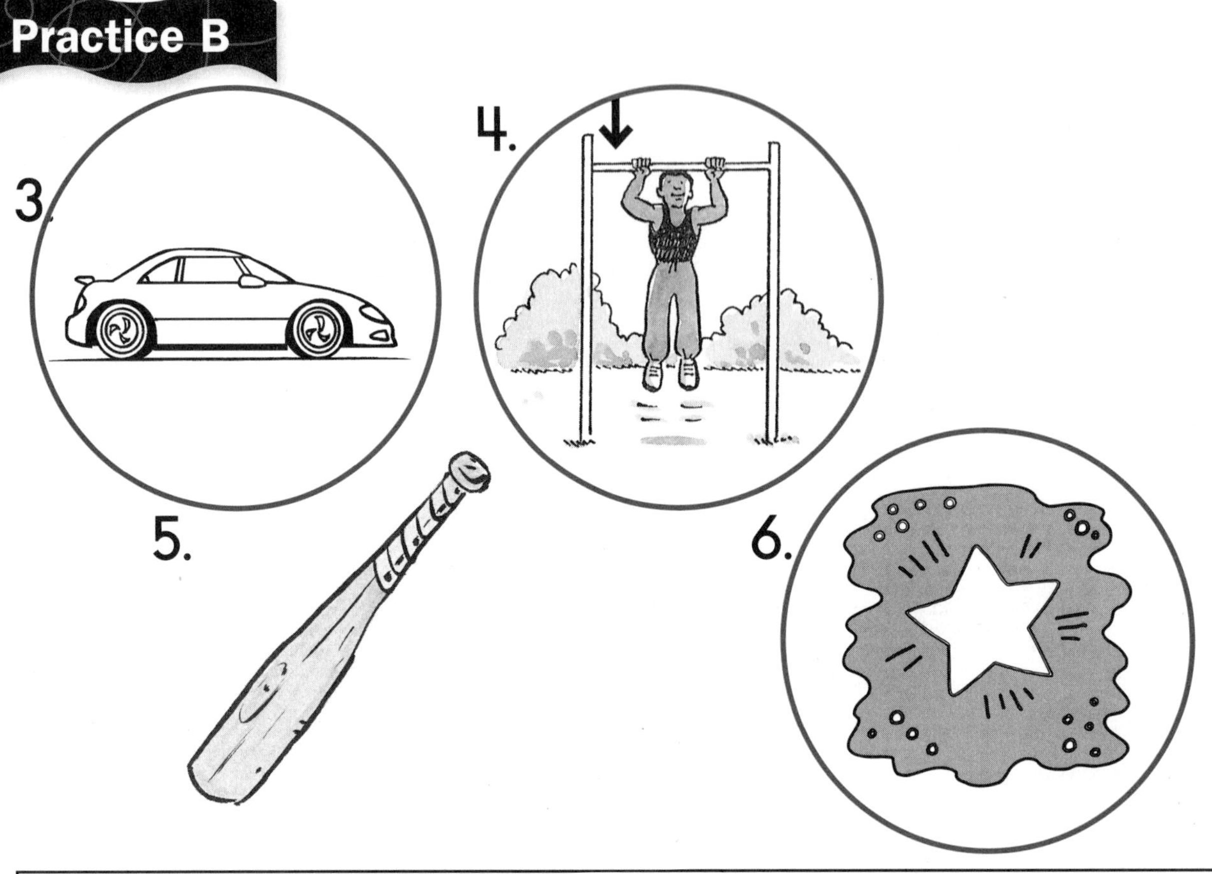

arm **card** **jar**

7.

card

8.

jar

9.

arm

Name ______________________________ Date ________

Sounds and Spellings

Practice A

Directions: Circle the sentence that goes with each picture. Write the last sentence on the line.

1. 

Mom gave Ben a new wallet.

Mom gave Ben a new watch.

2. 

The cat has a limp.

The cat is on the limb.

3. 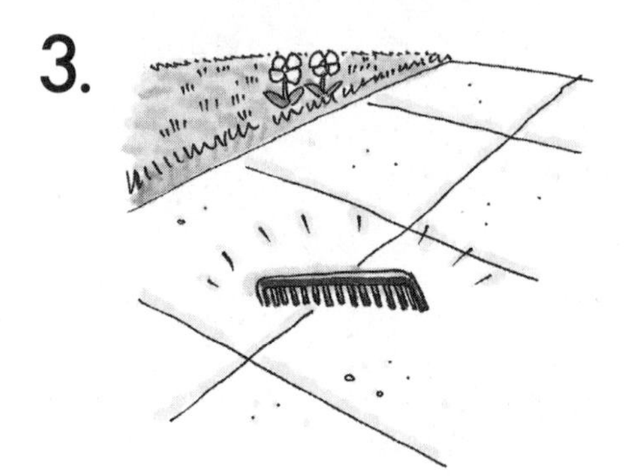

The comb is on the sidewalk.

The cone is on the sidewalk.

The comb is on the sidewalk.

Practice B

Directions: Write the correct word in each space.

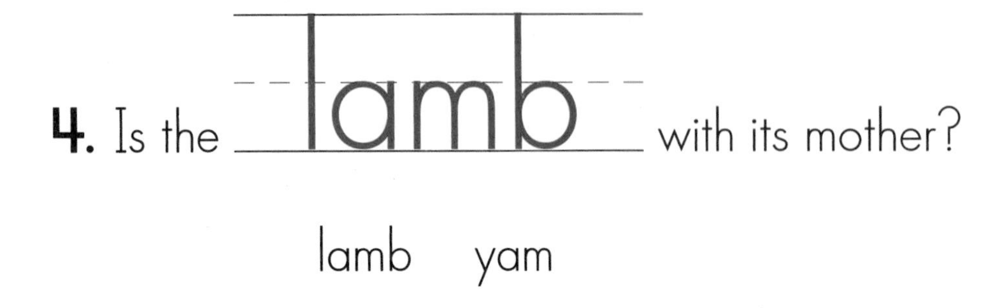

4. Is the ______ with its mother?

lamb yam

5. Did he ______ his hands?

wish wash

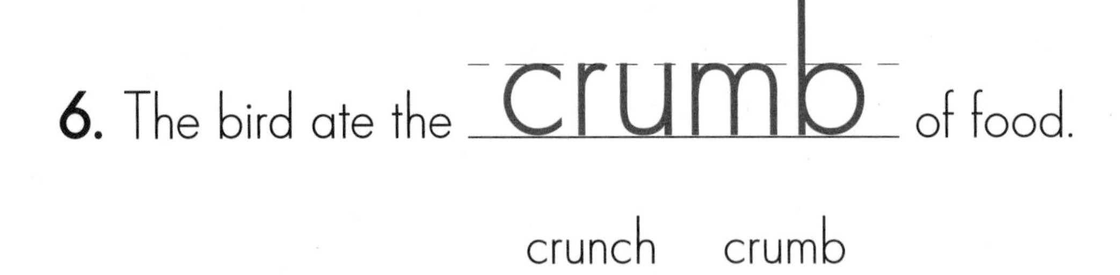

6. The bird ate the ______ of food.

crunch crumb

7. I want to have a glass of ______.

water waiter

Name ______________________ Date ________

Sounds and Spellings

Directions: Practice writing *w* and *W*. Then, draw two pictures whose names begin with the /w/ sound.

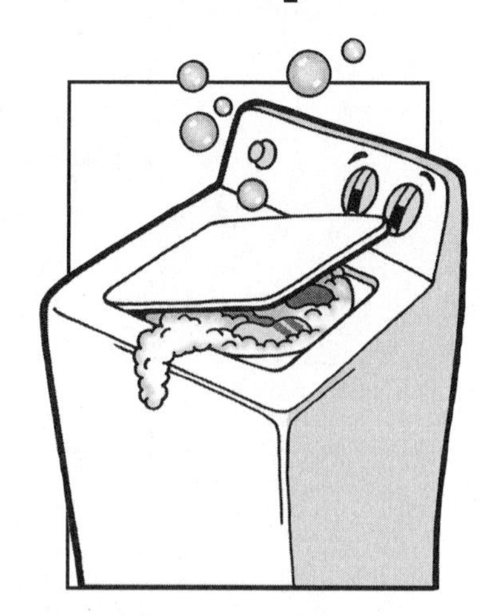

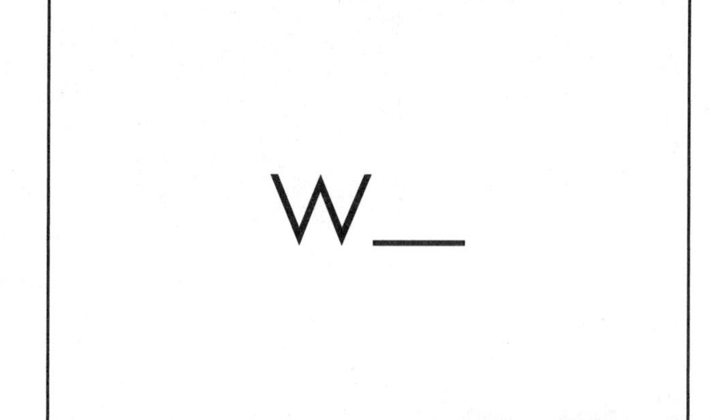

Practice A

w w w w w

W W W W W

1. Answers will vary. Picture must begin with the /w/ sound.

2. Answers will vary. Picture must begin with the /w/ sound.

Sounds and Spellings

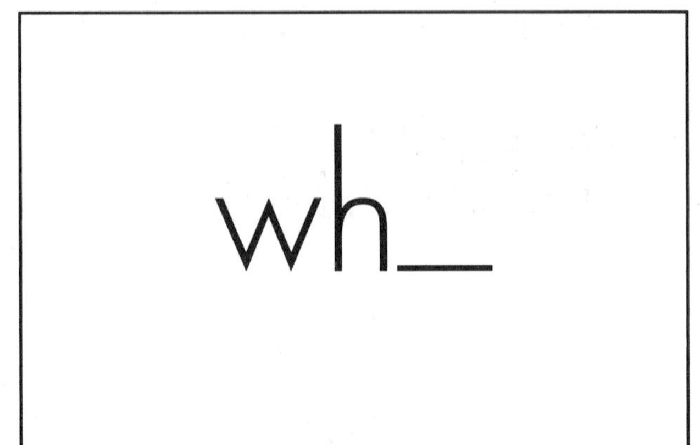

Directions: Practice writing *wh* and *Wh*. Copy the word. Then, draw a picture whose name begins with the /wh/ sound.

Practice B

wh wh wh wh wh

Wh Wh Wh Wh Wh

whip whip

3. Answers will vary. Picture must begin with the /wh/ sound.

Name ______________________ **Date** ________

Telling Sentences

Focus

Rule Sentences start with a capital letter. Sentences that tell something end with periods.

Practice A

Directions: Read the sentences. Circle the period at the end of each sentence. Then, read the next set of sentences. Draw a line under the last word in each sentence. Add a period to each sentence.

1. I sat on Pam's hat.
2. A ham is in the pan.
3. Max fell down the hill.

---

4. She ran on this path ___
5. An ant nips at the plant ___
6. Sid stands on his hands ___

Practice B

Directions: Write the telling sentences. Start with a capital letter. End with a period.

7. bob is at bat

Bob is at bat.

8. bob taps the bat

Bob taps the bat.

9. bob hits the ball

Bob hits the ball.

10. He runs and wins.

He runs and wins.

Name ______________________ Date ________

Directions: Practice writing *er, ir,* and *ur.* Copy the words.

Sounds and Spellings

er
ir
ur

Practice A

er er er er er

ir ir ir ir ir

ur ur ur ur ur

herd herd shirt shirt

Practice B

Directions: Unscramble the words in the box and write the sentence correctly on the line. Say the name of each picture to the student. Have the student write the name of each picture and underline the /er/ spelling.

bird.	is	her	It

It is her bird.

dirt fern hurt

Name ________________________ Date ________

Sounds and Spellings Review

Practice A

Directions: Write the word that goes with each picture.

chin	her	curl	wag

1.

chin

2.

curl

3.

wag

4.

her

Practice B

Directions: Circle the correct word and write the name of each picture. Have the student write the name of each picture and underline the spellings of /ch/, /ar/, and /ir/.

5.

Bob has a pet.

pet
bird

6.

Pat sees a star.

star
car

7.

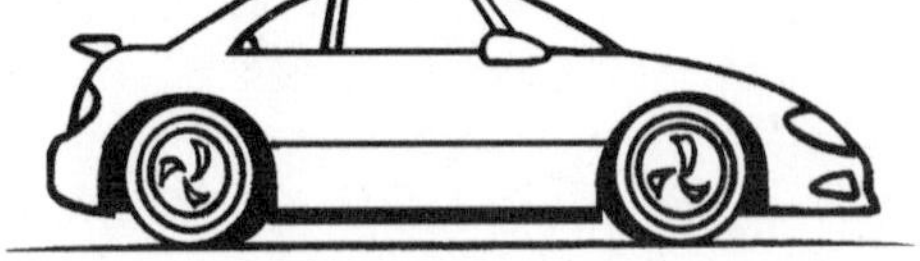

patch car bird

Name ____________________ Date ________

Sounds and Spellings

Directions: Read the words. Circle the vowel letter that makes the schwa sound in each word and put a dot over it. Then connect each word to its picture.

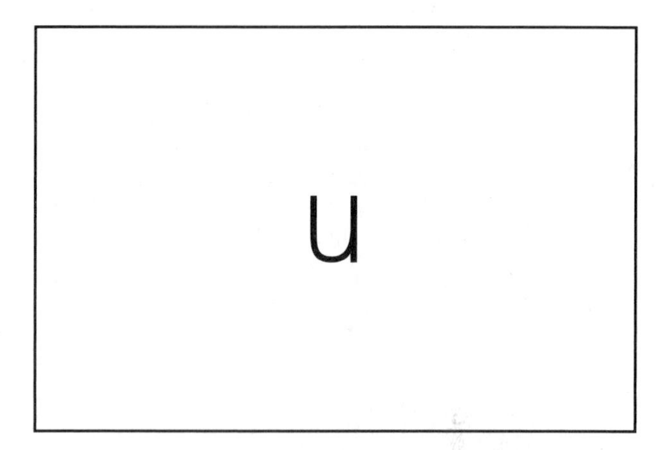

Practice A

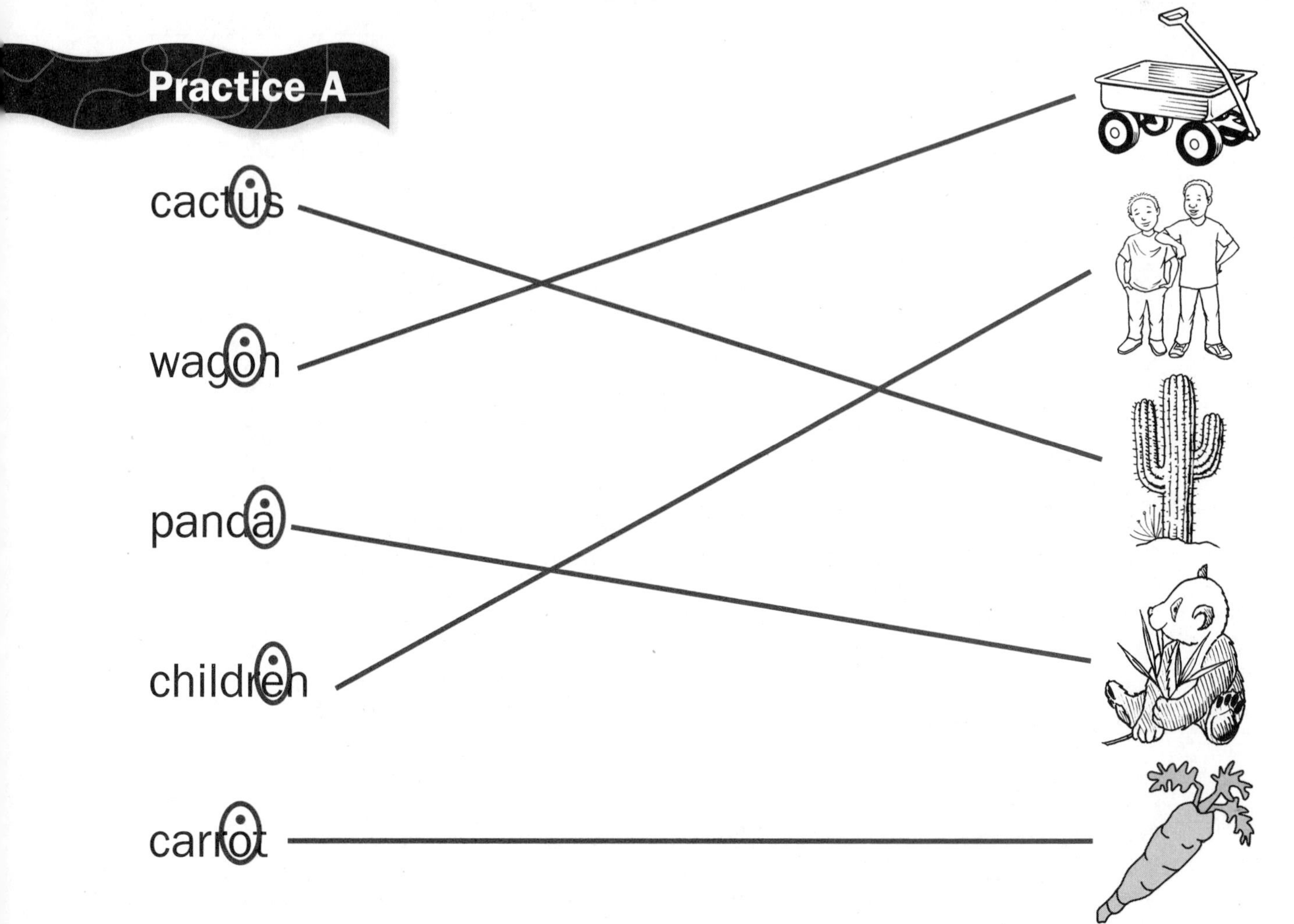

Lesson 11

Practice B

Directions: On the blank lines, write the word from the box that names each picture. Put a dot above the vowel letter that makes the schwa sound.

melon	cotton	banana	gallop

1. cotton

2. gallop

3. banana

4. melon

Name ______________________________ Date __________

Directions: Trace the schwa spellings. Then, write them on the lines as you say the sounds.

Sounds and Spellings

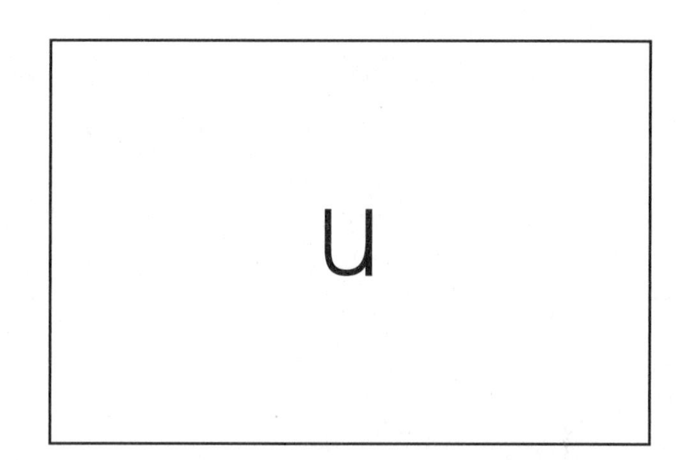

Practice A

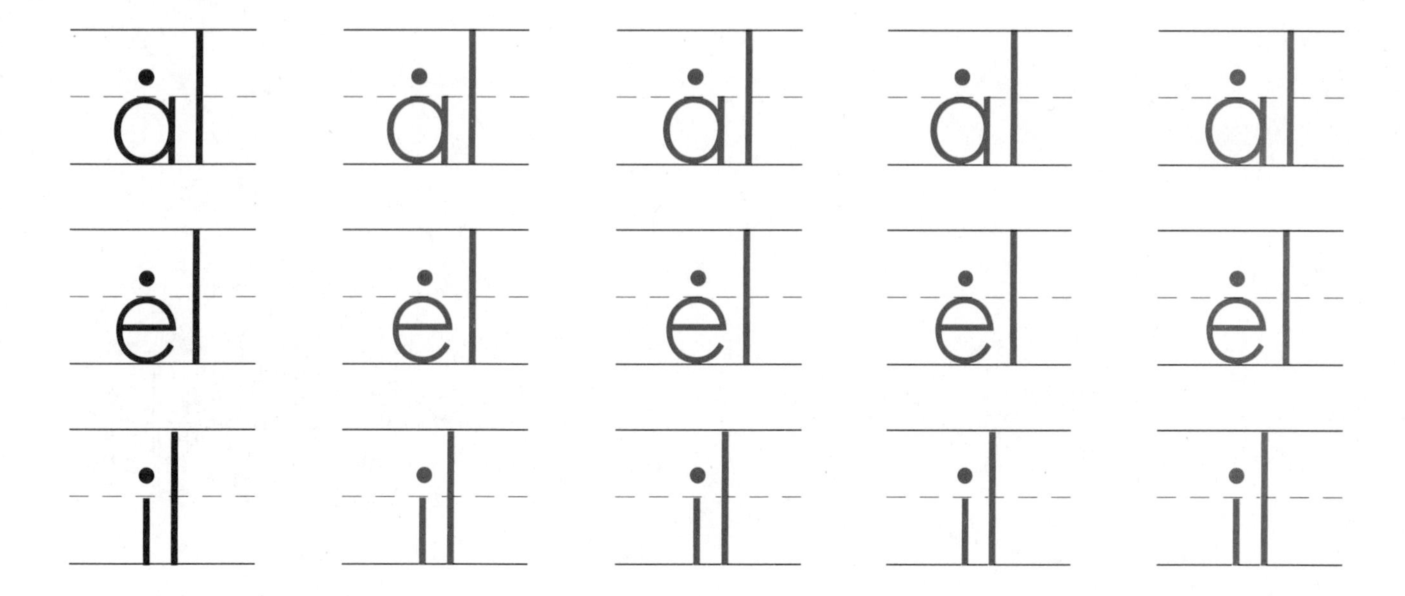

Practice B

Directions: Read the words. Circle the vowel letter that makes the schwa sound in each word and put a dot over it. Then connect each word to its picture.

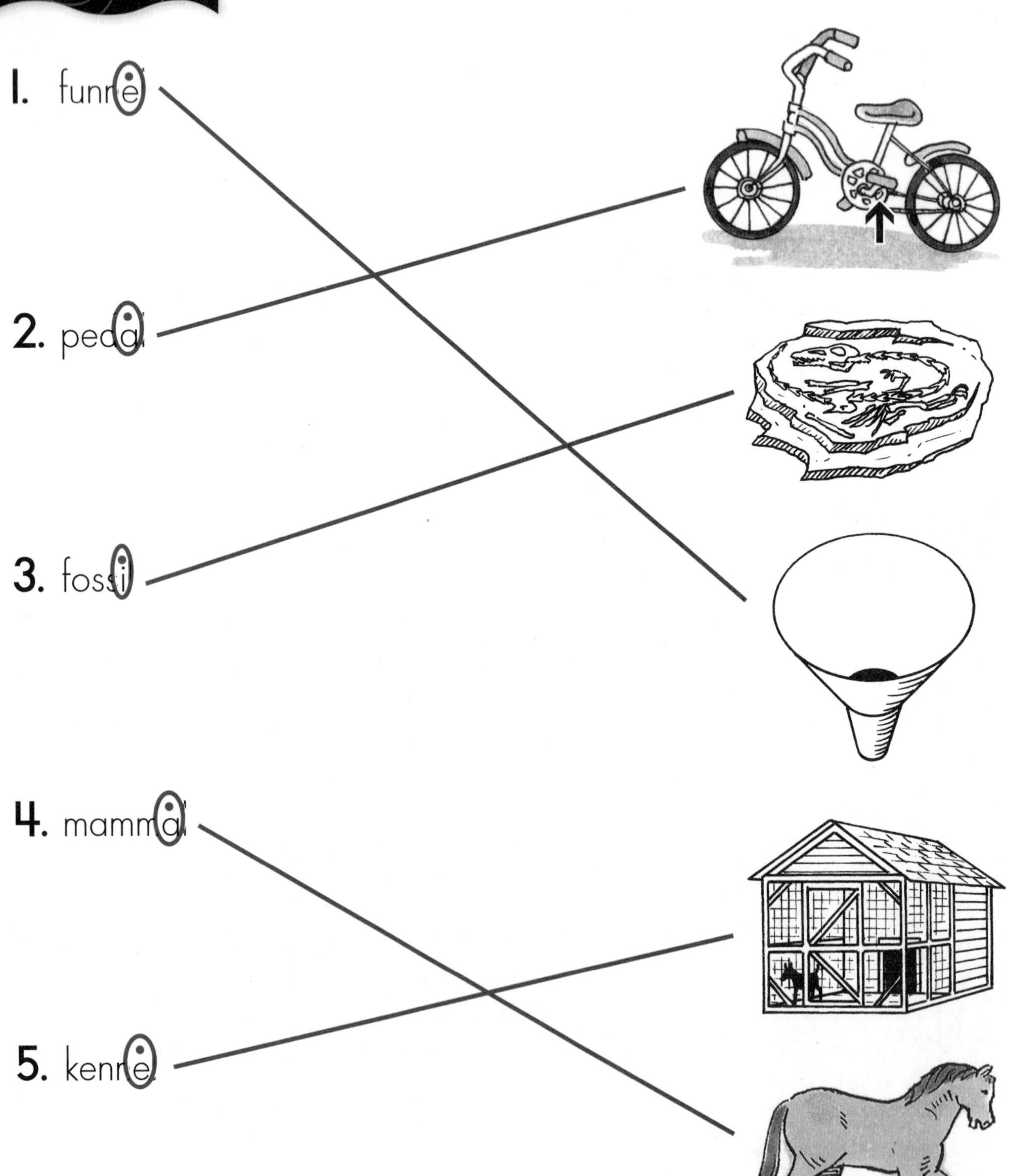

Name ______________________ Date ________

Sounds and Spellings

Directions: Practice writing *ng* and *nk*. Copy the words.

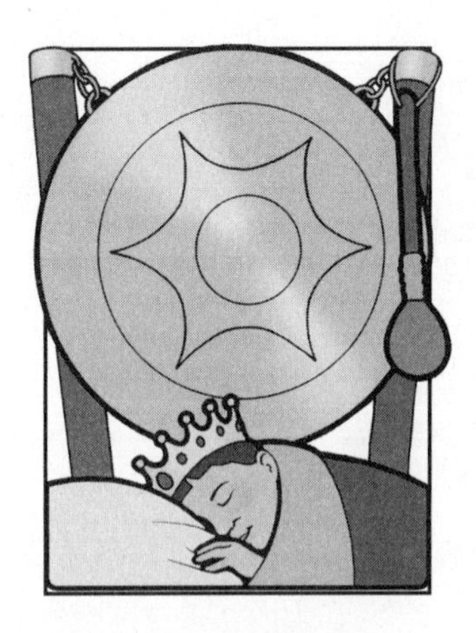

Practice A

ng ng ng ng ng

bring bring ring ring

skunk skunk think think

Practice B

Directions: Write the sentence shown by each picture. Say the name of each picture to the student. Have the student write the name of each picture and underline the spellings of /ng/ or /nk/.

1. 

The ring is big.

He sings.

The ring is big.

2. 

It has wings.

He swings.

He swings.

3.

ring

king

sink

Name ______________________ Date ________

Writing Questions

Focus

Rule Sentences that ask something are called **questions**. A sentence that asks a question **(?)** ends with a question mark.

Practice A

Directions: Read the sentences. Circle the question mark at the end of each sentence. Then read the next set of sentences. Draw a line under the last word in each sentence and add a question mark.

1. Can the cat see the rat?
2. Did Dan nap in the van?
3. Will we get a cat?

---

4. Is Bud in the sun?
5. When will we go to the store?
6. What is in the box?

Practice B

Directions: Read the sentences. Draw a line under each sentence that asks a question. Circle the question marks.

7. Did she look in the trash?

8. Do the shirts have dots?

9. The shirts have dots.

10. Can you run up that hill?

11. Is the car in the barn?

12. The car is in the barn.

Name ______________________ Date ________

Directions: Practice writing *qu* and *Qu*. Write each of the words on the lines.

Sounds and Spellings

qu_

Practice A

qu qu qu qu qu

Qu Qu Qu Qu Qu

quilt quilt quit quit

Practice B

Directions: Look at the picture. Circle the correct word that describes the picture. Write the sentence for the last one.

1. 

quit 

2. 

squint 

3. 

A quick squirrel ran.

A quick squirrel ran.

Name ______________________ Date ________

Sounds and Spellings Review

Practice A

Directions: Say the name of each picture. Read the partial word. Say the sound for each spelling and try it in the partial word to see if it makes sense. Circle the spelling that finishes each word.

 1. qu ack qu nk	 4. nick el mp el	 7. wi ng ng nk
 2. chipmu nk nk ng	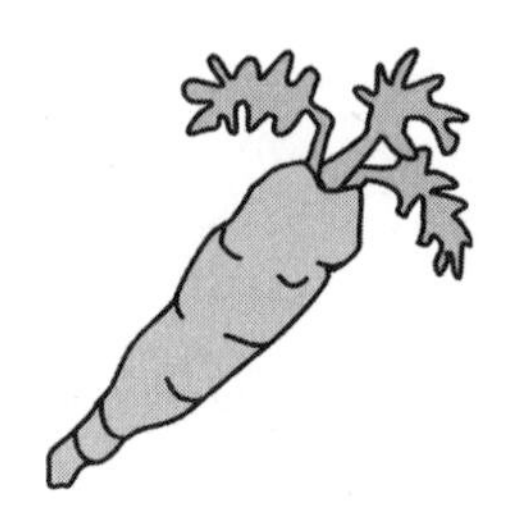 5. carr o t o p	 8. pand a __ ir a
 3. qu ilt th qu	 6. anim al al th	 9. ta nk nk ng

Practice B

Directions: Read each sentence. Circle the word that completes the sentence.

10. Mitch did not think camp was fun.

think pink

11. Trish had a pink tent for camping.

pick pink

12. Hank drank a quart of milk.

drink drank

13. The ducks went swimming in the pond.

swimming swinging

14. The big cat is king of the animal kingdom.

kick king kingdom

Name ______________________ Date ________

Directions: Practice writing *V* and saying the sound it makes. Read and write the words. Then practice writing *Y* and saying the sound it makes. Read and write the words.

Sounds and Spellings

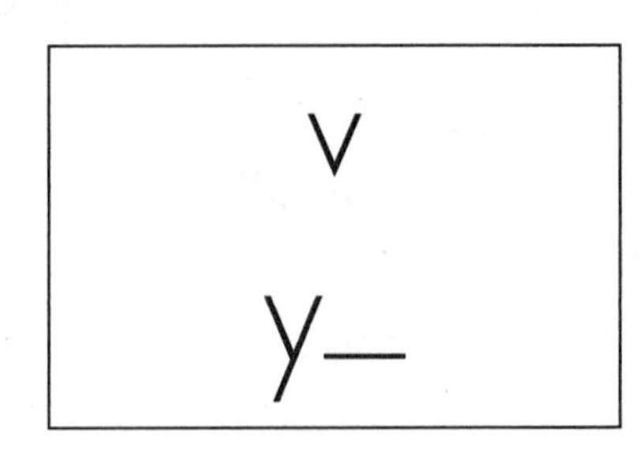

Practice A

Vv Vv Vv Vv Vv

van van vet vet

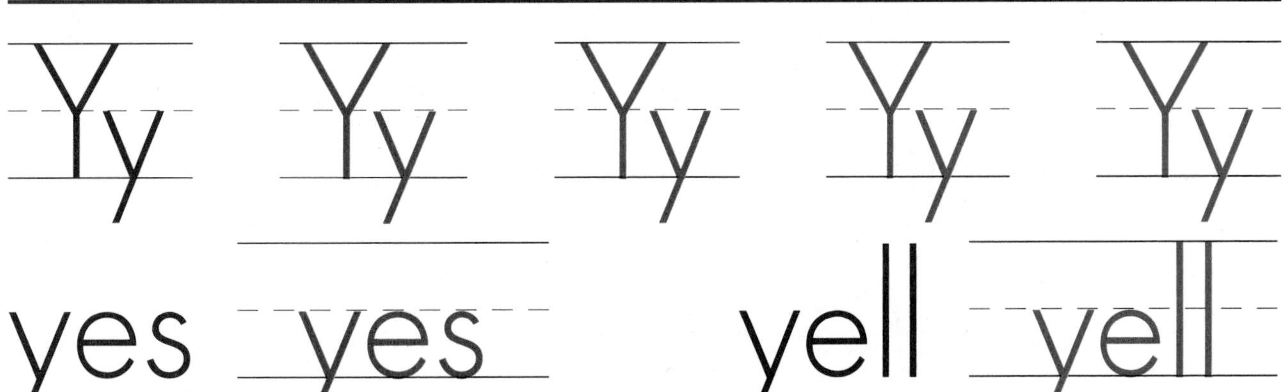

Lesson 1

Practice B

Directions: Play Riddle Me This! Say the sound for each card pictured. Blend the sounds to make a word. Write the spellings and then the word. Then choose a word to finish the sentence. Circle the word.

word

 ar  yarn

word

v er 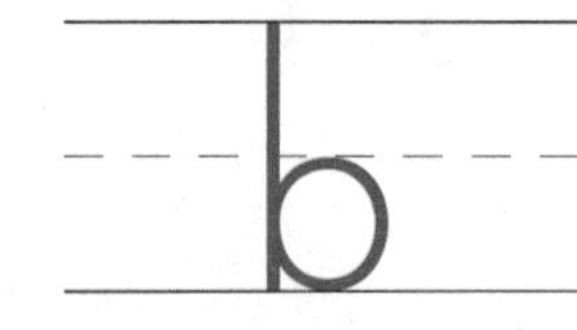 verb

Viv smelled the  in the oven.

yums (yams)

Name ____________________ Date ________

Sounds and Spellings

Directions: Finish the words by writing le on the blank lines. Read each word and draw a line from the word to the picture it names.

The syllable ***-le***

Practice A

cand l e

freck l e s

thimb l e

gigg l e

sprink l e

Practice B

Directions: Read each sentence. Circle the best word to complete the sentences.

1. Val lit the candles for Mom.

2. Lots of stars twinkle when it is dark.

3. The cat tangles the yarn a lot.

4. Jack wiggled the jar to get the bug out.

UNIT 4 Lesson 3

Name ______________________ Date ________

Exclamatory Sentences

Focus

Rule Some sentences show strong feeling. They end with an exclamation point. !

Practice A

Directions: Read the sentences. Circle the exclamation point at the end of each sentence. Then read the second set of sentences. Draw a line under the last word in each sentence. Then add an exclamation point.

1. Look out, that ball will hit you!

2. A big bug is in that jar!

3. This cat is bad!

---

4. Help, the bird is hurt!

5. What a big cat you have!

6. Tim hit the ball hard!

Telling, Asking, and Exclamatory Sentences

Focus

Rule Telling sentences end with periods. **.** Asking sentences end with question marks. **?** Exclamatory sentences end with exclamation points. **!**

Practice B

Directions: Read each sentence. Put the correct mark at the end.

1. The hat is in the basket .
2. Will you go to the farm ?
3. A big rat is in the barn !
4. What can I do to help you ?
5. Six pals went to the mall .
6. This pot is hot !

Name ______________________ Date ________

Sounds and Spellings

Directions: Copy the words in the spaces provided. Then write other words with the /ā/ sound spelled *a* or *a_e*.

a
a_e

Practice A

ate ate

tape tape

Words will vary but must have the /ā/ sound spelled *a* or *a_e*.

Practice B

Directions: Circle the correct word to complete each sentence. Say the name of each picture to the student. Have the student write the name of each picture and underline the spelling of the /ā/ sound.

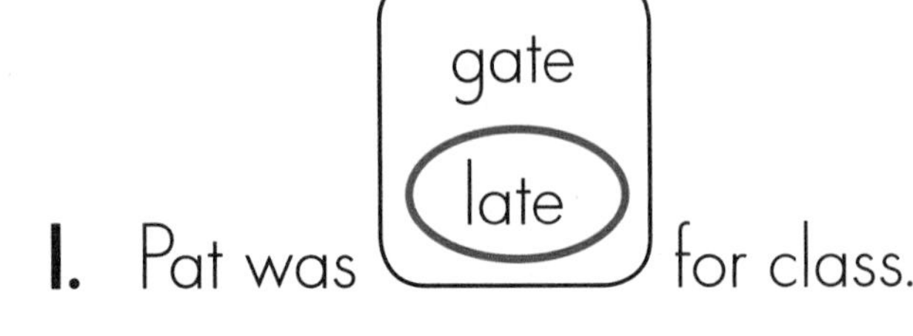

1. Pat was [gate / late] for class.

2. Sam swam in the [lake / flake].

3. Let's play a [game / same].

gate

rake

cake

Name ______________________ **Date** ________

Sounds and Spellings Review

Practice A

Directions: Say the name of each picture. Write the names on the blank lines.

1. 
yard

2. 
giggle

3. 
vest

4. 
candle

5. 
yell

6. 
table

7. 
whale

8. 
van

9. 
ape

Practice B

10. Steven and Dale baked cupcakes.

11. Viv has big dimples.

12. Ava yelled for her cat.

13. The yak ate a little grass.

14. The bats went into the dark cave.

Name ______________________ Date ________

Sounds and Spellings

Directions: Write each word. Write four more words that have the long i sound spelled *i* or *i_e*.

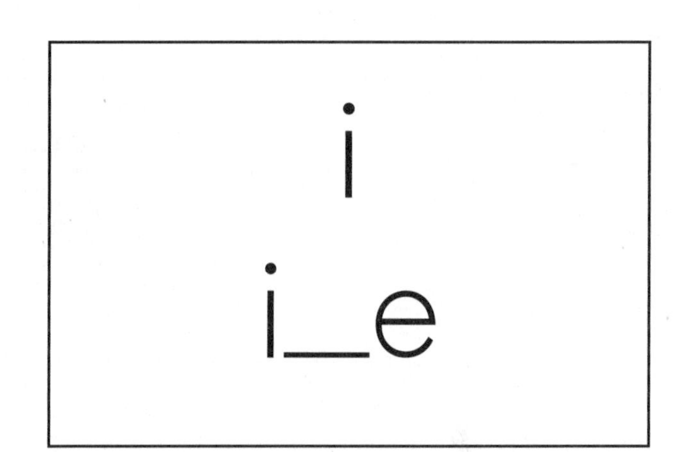

Practice A

fine fine

pile pile

Words will vary but must have the /ī/ sound spelled *i* or *i_e*.

Practice B

Directions: Complete each sentence with the correct word from the box.

1. The lime is ripe.

limp
lime

2. We must stand in line.

lane
line

3. Jen rides her bike.

bike
bake

4. My dog does not bite.

bit
bite

Name ________________ Date ________

Sounds and Spellings

Directions: Practice writing *ce* and *ci* and copy the words below. Then draw a picture whose name has the /s/ sound spelled *ce* or *ci_*.

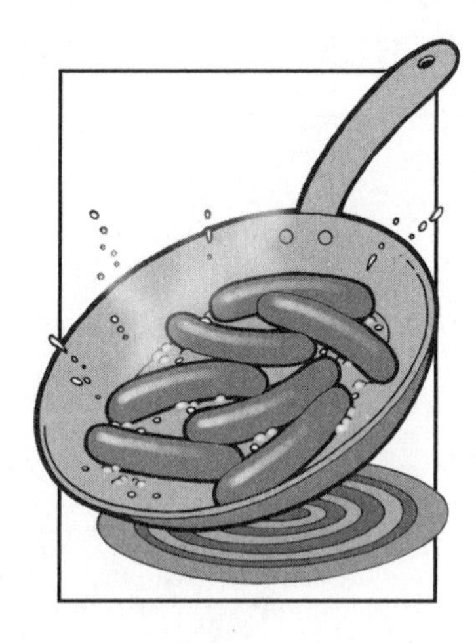

ce
ci_

Practice A

ce ce ce ce ce

ci ci ci ci ci

race race

circle circle

Answers will vary. Picture must have the /s/ sound spelled *ce* or *ci_*.

UNIT 4 Lesson 8

Practice B

base	rake	cane	pace

Directions: List each word under the ***Sound/Spelling Card*** picture for the /s/ sound or /k/ sound.

base rake

pace cane

Name ______________________________ **Date** ________

Imperative Sentences

Focus

Rule Imperative sentences are used to give an order, make a request or demand, or express a wish. They can end with a period or exclamation point.

Practice A

Directions: Read the sentences and underline the last word. Add a period to the first three sentences and an exclamation point to the bottom sentences.

1. Help Gran get up .
2. Take me to the store .
3. Walk the pup .

---

4. Yell for help !
5. Get that big bug !
6. Sit down and stop it !

Practice B

Directions: Listen as your teacher reads each sentence aloud using appropriate expression to suggest desired punctuation. Follow along, think about what is read and write appropriate punctuation.

7. Stop the car now !

8. Pass the paper to Val .

9. Surprise !

10. Pick your best letter .

11. Catch that big spider !

12. Ride your bike with Sis .

Name ______________________ Date ________

Sounds and Spellings

Directions: Practice writing *ge* and *gi_*. Copy the word.

ge
gi_

Practice A

ge ge ge ge ge

gi gi gi gi gi

ginger ginger

Lesson 9

Practice B

Directions: Read the words in the box. Write each word under the correct ***Sound/Spelling Card.*** Say the name of each picture to the student. Have the student write the name of each picture and underline the spelling of the /j/ sound.

rug	germ	game	stage

1\.

germ

stage

2\.

rug

game

3\.

gerbil

page

cage

Name ______________________________ **Date** ________

Sounds and Spellings Review

Practice A

Directions: Say the name of the pictures. Listen for /s/ or /k/. Draw a line to connect the picture to the sound you hear. Write the name of the picture on the blank lines. At the bottom, write the name of the picture on the blank lines.

Practice B

Directions: Read the sentences. Circle the correct word to complete each one. Then say the sound for the cards pictured. Blend the sounds to make the word. Write the spellings and then the word.

1. Lance slid on the ice.

   (slid) slide

2. Ida will chill the hot fudge.

   child (chill)

3. The mice ate Madge's gingerbread.

   (mice) nice

word bridge

Name ____________________ Date ________

Directions: Copy the words in the spaces provided. Then write other words with the /ō/ sound spelled o or o_e.

Sounds and Spellings

o

o_e

Practice A

no no

bone bone

Words will vary but must have the /ō/ sound spelled *o* or *o_e*.

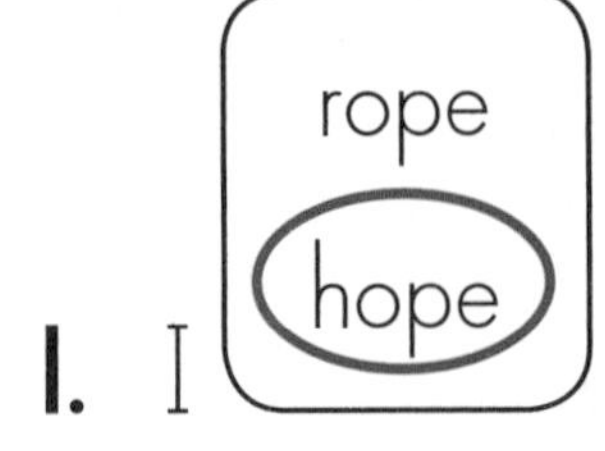

Directions: Circle the word that best completes each sentence. Say the name of each picture to the student. Have the student write the name of each picture and underline the spelling of Long o.

1. I [rope / hope] the sun is out.

2. Dad can lift a [stone / hope].

cone

rope

Name ______________________ **Date** ________

Adjectives That Compare

Focus

Rule Add *-er* to an adjective to compare two things.

Add *-est* to an adjective to compare more than two things.

Practice A

Directions: Look at the pictures and write the word that correctly describes each one. Then complete each sentence with the correct word.

fast	faster	fastest	older	oldest

fast faster fastest

1. My grandpa is the oldest.

2. My dad is older than my brother.

UNIT 4 Lesson 13

Practice B

Directions: Look at the pictures. Write *small, smaller, smallest* to describe each one. Then read the sentences. Choose *longer* or *longest* to complete each one correctly.

small	**smaller**	**smallest**
	longer	**longest**

small smaller smallest

1. An arm is longer than a hand.

2. A leg is longest.

Name ______________________ Date ________

Directions: Copy the words in the spaces provided. Then write other words with the /ū/ sound spelled *u* or *u_e*.

Sounds and Spellings

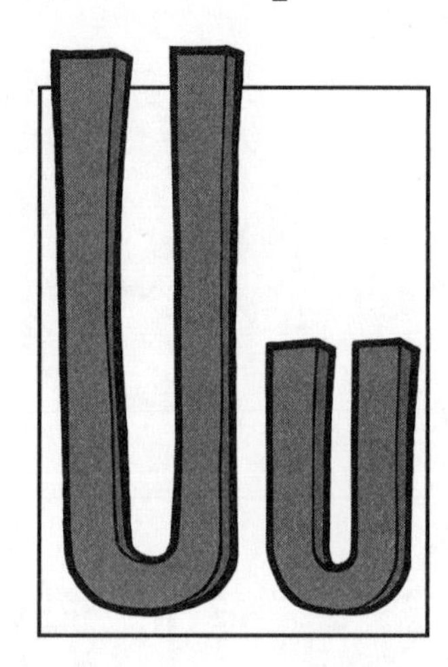

u
u_e

Practice A

cute cute cube cube

Words will vary but must have the /ū/ sound spelled *u* or *u_e.*

Practice B

Directions: Circle the sentence described by the picture and write it on the line. Say the name of each picture to the student. Have the student write the name of each picture and underline the spelling of the /ū/ sound.

(The ice cubes melt.)

The mule is cute.

The ice cubes melt.

music mule menu

Name ______________________ Date ________

Sounds and Spellings Review

Directions: Say the name of the pictures. Write the word that names the picture. Then read the sentences. Circle the word to complete each sentence.

o

o_e

Practice A

clock

rope

smoke

smock

1. Opal wore a homemade robe.

rob robe

2. The robot opened the note.

note not

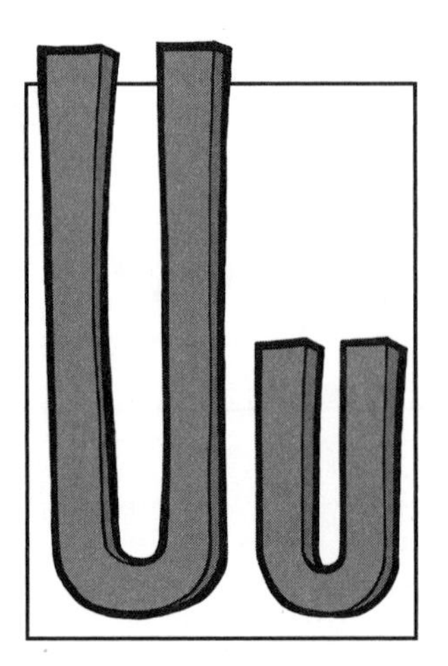

u

u_e

Directions: Say the name of the pictures. Write the word that names the picture. Then read the sentences. Circle the word that completes each sentence.

Practice B

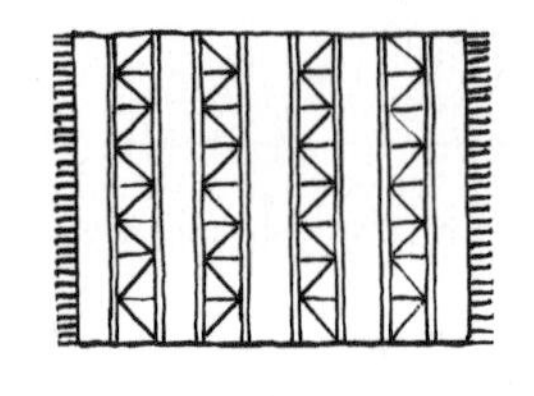

rug mule cub cube

1. Hugo used a bugle to wake us.

used fused

2. The weather can be humid in summer.

humid human

Name ____________________ Date ________

Sounds and Spellings

Directions: Write the words. Then write other words with the /ē/ sound spelled *e* or *e_e*.

Ee

e

e_e

Practice A

me me me

theme theme theme

1. Words will vary, but must have the /ē/ sound spelled *e* or *e_e*.
2. ____________________
3. ____________________
4. ____________________

Practice B

Directions: Look at each picture. Read the two sentences. Circle the sentence that tells about the picture. For the last picture, write the sentence you circled.

5. 

He sang the theme song.

He broke the meter.

6. 

She sits on a bench.

She is an athlete.

7. 

We compete.

We sit on a trapeze.

8. We compete.

Name ______________________ Date ________

Capitalization

Focus

Rule Names of people, *I*, special things, and special places begin with **capital letters**.

Example **Tia** and **I** went to **Grant Park**.

Practice A

Directions: Listen as your teacher reads each word. Write it on the line. Capitalize the letter in each word that should be capital.

1. i I
2. marcy Marcy
3. kennedy park Kennedy Park
4. rocky mountains Rocky Mountains
5. woodland school Woodland School

Practice B

Directions: Read each sentence. Circle the letters that should be capital. Then write the word or words correctly on the line.

6. Mike and i went to the baseball game.

I

7. My family spent a day at washington park.

8. Nate and amy walked to the store.

9. Nancy sang at wilson school.

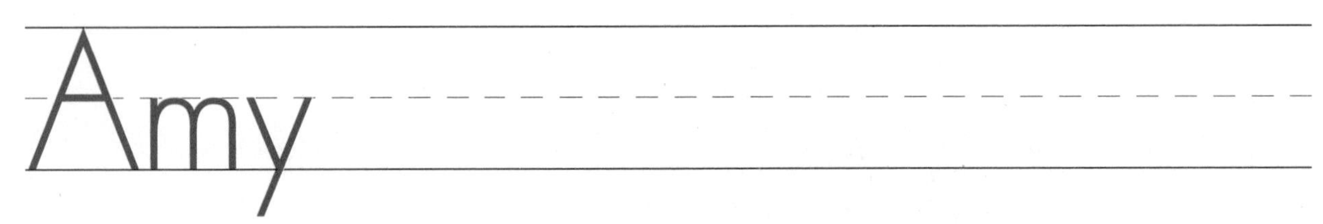

Name ______________________ Date ________

Sounds and Spellings

Directions: Practice writing *ee* and *ea*. Write the words. Then write other words with the /ē/ sound spelled *ee* or *ea*.

ee

ea

Practice A

ee ee ee ee ee

ea ea ea ea ea

beep beep tea tea

1. Words will vary, 2. but must have the /ē/ sound spelled *ee* or *ea*.

Practice B

Directions: Read the words in the box. Write the word that names each picture. Then underline the long e spelling in each word.

beak	heel	peach	peas	seal	street

3.  seal

4.  peach

5.  heel

6.  peas

7.  beak

8. 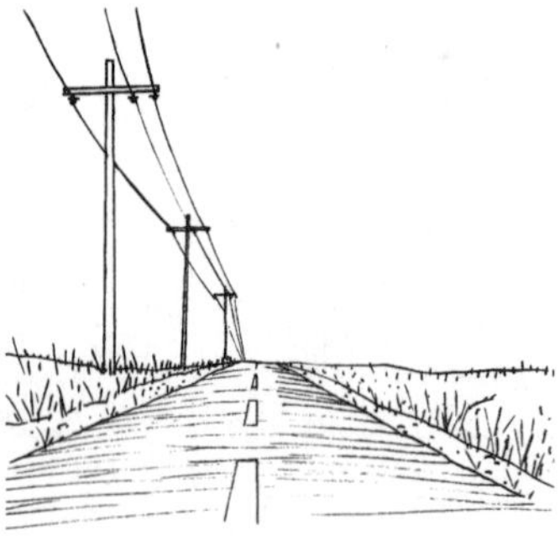 street

Name ______________________ Date ________

Sounds and Spellings

Focus The **long e** sound can be spelled **e, e_e, ea,** or **ee**.

Examples be Pete pea beep

Practice A

Directions: Write the long e spellings to finish each word. Then read the words.

1. 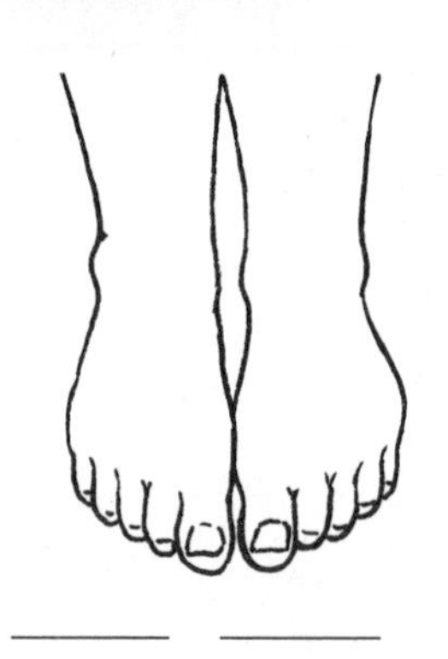

f__e__ __e__t

2. 

tr__e__ __e__

3. 

sh__e__ __e__p

4. 

l__e__ __a__f

5. 

s__e__ __a__l

6. 

r__e__ __a__d

Practice B

Directions: Read each word. Circle the long e spelling. Then draw a picture of each word.

7. Drawing should depict meat.

meat

8. Drawing should depict a bee.

bee

9. Drawing should depict a wheel.

wheel

10. Drawing should depict beads.

beads

11. Drawing should depict a flea.

12. Drawing should depict a seed.

seed

Name ______________________ **Date** ________

Sounds and Spellings

Directions: Practice writing y and ie. Copy the words. Then write other words with the /ē/ sound spelled _y or _ie_.

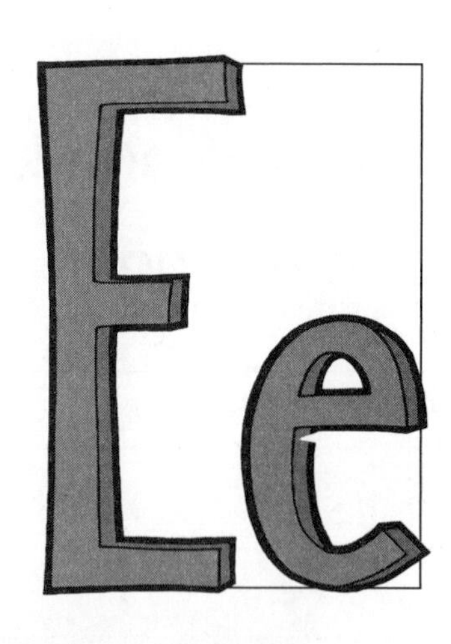

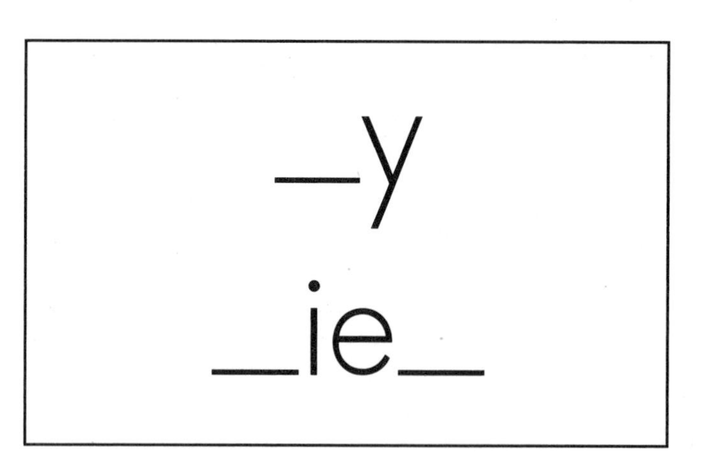

Practice A

y y y y y

ie ie ie ie ie

city city

field field

1. Words will vary, 2. but must have the /ē/ sound spelled _y or _ie_.

Practice B

Directions: Look at each picture. Read the two sentences. Circle the sentence that describes the picture. For the last picture, write the sentence you circled.

3. 

The guppies swim in the pond.

The guppy swims in the pond.

4. 

Her niece is funny.

Her kitty is funny.

5. 

Andy eats a piece of cake.

Andy pats a bunny.

6. Andy pats a bunny.

Name ______________________ Date ________

Capitalization and Commas

Focus

Rule Days and months begin with a **capital letter**. A **comma** comes after the date.

Example **M**onday **J**uly 4, 2009

Practice A

Directions: Read each date. Write it on the line. Capitalize the letter in each word that should be capital. Add a comma where it belongs.

1. saturday Saturday
2. friday Friday
3. december December
4. june 18 2010 June 18, 2010
5. january 1 2000 January 1, 2000

Practice B

Directions: Read each sentence. Circle each letter that should be a capital. Then write the capital letter above it. The first one is done for you. Add a comma where it belongs.

S M

1. Today is the first saturday in may.

J A

2. The fruit stand is open in july and august.

T T

3. Music class is on tuesdays and thursdays.

F M

4. This year soccer starts on friday, march 6.

D J

5. It usually snows in december and january.

D

6. This year winter starts on december 20 2010.

^ ,

Name ______________________________ Date ________

Directions: Read the words in the box. Write the word that names each picture. You will not use all the words. Underline the spelling for the /s/ sound in each word.

Sounds and Spellings

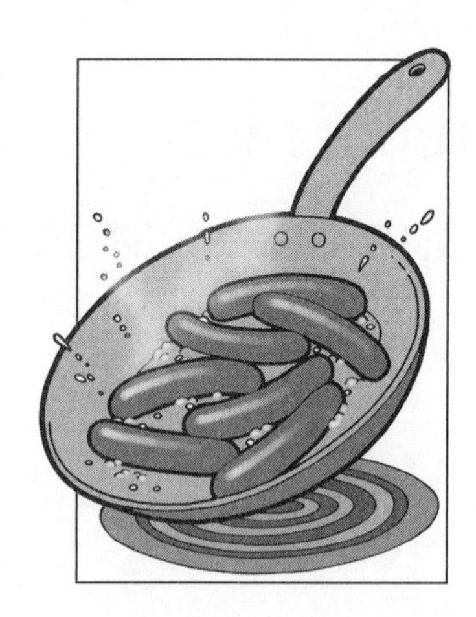

s
ce
ci_
cy

Practice A

city	fence	lacy	mice	seal	swing

1. 

2. 

3. 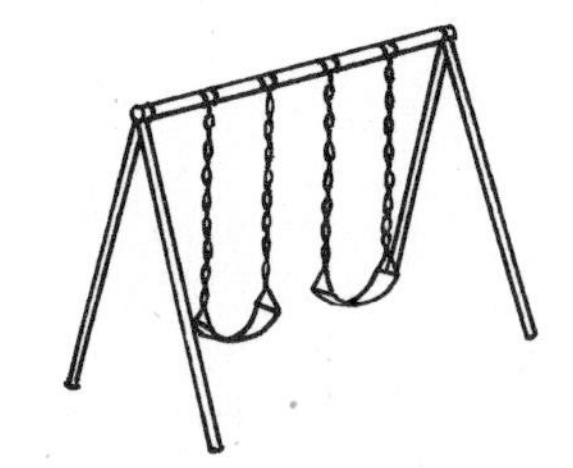

Practice B

Directions: Look at each picture. Read the sentences. Circle the sentence that describes the picture. For the last picture, write the sentence you circled. Circle the /s/ spellings in that sentence.

4. 

Marcy and Stacy run a race.

Marcy and Stacy drink ice water.

5. 

Scott likes to dance and sing.

Scott drove to the city.

6. 

Nancy eats grapes.

Nancy has a fancy sweater.

7. Nancy has a fancy sweater.

Name ______________________________ Date ________

Sounds and Spellings

Focus

Long *e* spelled _y and _ie_

Ss spelled s, ce, ci_, and cy

Practice A

_y | **_ie_**

1. cherr y

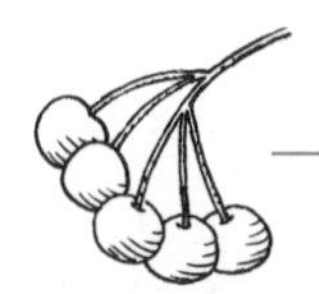

5. cherr ie s

2. pon y

6. pon ie s

3. bab y

7. bab ie s

4. bunn y

8. bunn ie s

Marcy and Nancy ate spicy meat.

Directions: Write the long e spelling to finish each word. Read the words. Then draw a line from each picture to the word that names it. Next read the sentence. Circle all of the /s/ spellings.

Practice B

Directions: Read each sentence. Circle the word in the box that completes it. Write the word on the line.

9. Darcy rode a bus to the

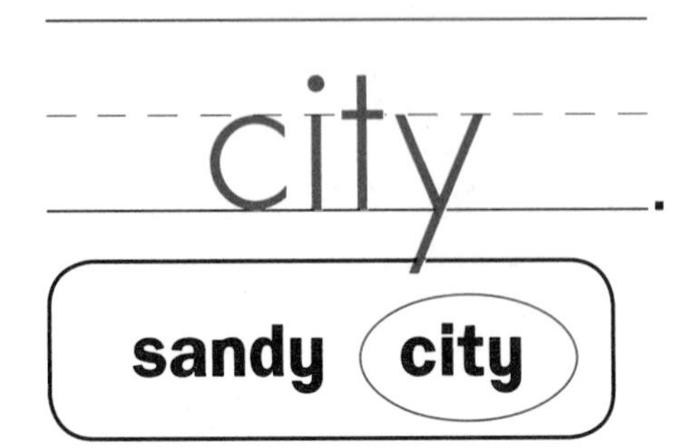

.

sandy | city

10. The ______ ate shiny red apples.

ponies | pansy

11. The weather was

and hot.

sunny | funny

Name ______________________ Date ________

Sounds and Spellings

Directions: Practice writing *ai* and *ay*. Write the words. Then write other words with the /ā/ sound spelled *ai_* or *_ay*.

ai_

_ay

Practice A

ai ai ai ai ai

ay ay ay ay ay

hay hay main main

1. Words will vary 2. but must have the /ā/ sound spelled *ai_* or *_ay.*

Practice B

Directions: Write the word that matches each picture.

3. 

mail may

mail

4. 

name nail

nail

5. 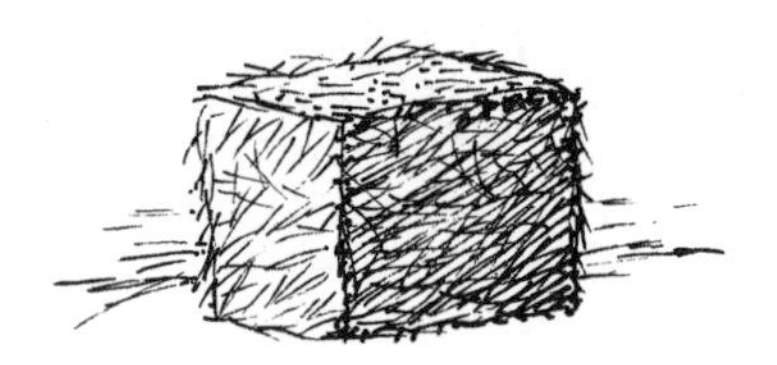

hay hail

hay

6. 

rain ray

rain

Name ______________________ **Date** ________

Plural Nouns

Focus

Rule To form the plural of a noun ending with a consonant and a **y**, change the **y** to **i**, then add **es**.

Examples **sky** → **skies**

bunny → **bunnies**

Practice A

Directions: Read each word. Write its plural form on the line next to it.

1. penny pennies
2. puppy puppies
3. city cities
4. community communities

Practice B

Directions: Read the words in the box. Write the name of each picture on the line.

babies	kitties	lilies	puppies

puppies

babies

kitties

lilies

Name ____________________ Date ________

Sounds and Spellings

Directions: Practice writing *y* and *ie*. Copy the words.

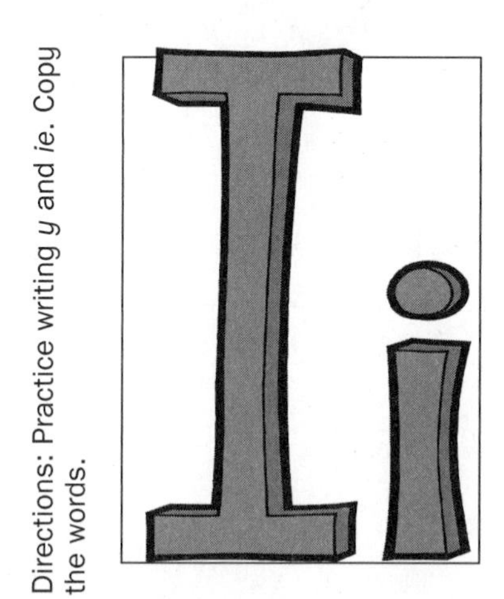

_igh

_y

_ie

Practice A

y y y y y

ie ie ie ie ie

igh igh igh igh igh

fry fry high high

UNIT 5 **Lesson 14**

Practice B

Directions: At the top, draw a line to connect the two words that go together. At the bottom, write the name of each picture and underline the /ī/ spelling.

tight	**time**
fire	**rope**
night	**fly**

1. tightrope
2. firefly
3. nighttime

4\. dries

5\. 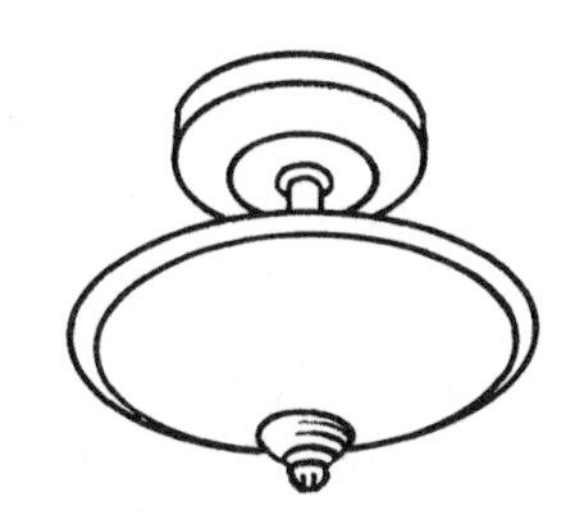 light

6\.  fly

Name ______________________ Date ________

Sounds and Spellings

Focus

Long *a* spelled ai_ and _ay

Long *i* spelled _igh, _y, and _ie

Practice A

Directions: Read each word. Circle the /ā/ or /ī/ spelling in each word. Then draw a picture of each word.

1. Drawing should depict a nail.

nail

2. Drawing should depict a tray.

tray

3. Drawing should depict a train.

train

4. Drawing should depict the sky.

sky

5. Drawing should depict a nightlight.

nightlight

6. Drawing should depict a highway.

highway

UNIT 5 Lesson 15

Practice B

Directions: Fill in the circle next to the word that best completes each sentence. Write the word on the line.

7. Day is not the same as night.

○ nail ● night

8. May I eat a piece of pie?

● pie ○ play

9. Ray has a bright red tie.

○ mail ● tie

10. The chain on my bike broke.

○ rain ● chain

Directions: Practice writing *oa*. Say the name of each picture to the student. Have the student write the name of each picture and underline the spelling of the /ō/ sound.

Name ______________________ Date ________

Sounds and Spellings

o
oa_

Practice

oa oa oa oa oa

1. road

2. goat

3. 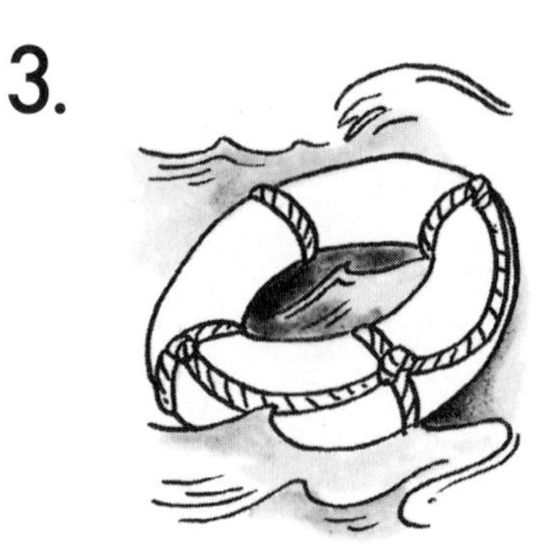
float

Sounds and Spellings

o

_ow

Directions: Practice writing ow. Copy the words. Then write other words with the /ō/ sound spelled oa_ or _ow.

Practice

ow ow ow ow ow

mow mow grow grow

1. 2. Words will vary but must have the /ō/ sound spelled *oa_* or *_ow.*

3. 4.

Name ______________________ **Date** ________

Capital Letters and Commas

Focus

Rule Names of cities, states, and countries begin with a capital letter and are separated by a comma.

Examples Dallas, Texas Orlando, Florida Rome, Italy

Practice A

Directions: Write the name of each city, state, or country beginning with a capital letter. Write the commas where they belong.

1. detroit michigan

Detroit, Michigan

2. lexington kentucky

Lexington, Kentucky

3. mexico city mexico

Mexico City, Mexico

UNIT 6 Lesson 3

Practice B

Directions: Read each sentence. Underline the words that should begin with a capital letter. Write the commas where they belong.

4. It is windy in chicago, illinois.

5. Many people live in los angeles, california.

6. There is a beach in miami, florida.

7. atlanta, georgia is the capital city of georgia.

8. wilmington, north carolina is in the south.

9. paris, france is a famous city.

Name ______________________________ **Date** ________

Sounds and Spellings

Directions: Practice writing *ew* and *ue*. Then write other words with the /ū/ sound spelled _*ew* or _*ue*.

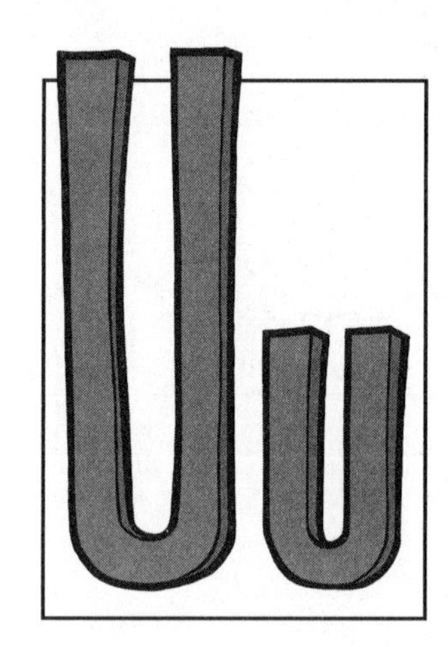

_ew
_ue

Practice A

ew ew ew ew ew

ue ue ue ue ue

1. ______________ 2. ______________
3. ______________ 4. ______________

Words will vary but must have the /u/ sound spelled *ew_* or *_ue.*

Practice B

Directions: Read the words in the box. Look at the pictures and read the sentences. Fill in the blank with the correct word.

value	rescue	few

5. A few leaves fell by the birdbath.

6. Sally will value the card you made.

7. Who will rescue the cat in the tree?

Name ______________________ **Date** ________

Sounds and Spellings

Practice A

Directions: Read each word. Listen to the vowel sound. Check the spelling. Write the word under the correct spelling.

argue blow cue curfew few float
goat mew row toad

oa_

1. 

2. 

3. 

_ew

6. curfew

7. few

8. mew

_ow

4. 

5. row

_ue

9. 

10. cue

Practice B

Directions: Look at the letters above each column and say the sound. Write those letters on the lines to make a word. Then, say the word.

_ew

11. f e w

12. p e w

13. m e w

_ue

14. c u e

15. h u e

16. resc u e

oa_

17. b o a t

18. g o a t

19. fl o a t

_ow

20. sn o w

21. bl o w

22. gr o w

Name ______________________ **Date** ________

Sounds and Spellings

Directions: Draw lines to match the words and pictures.

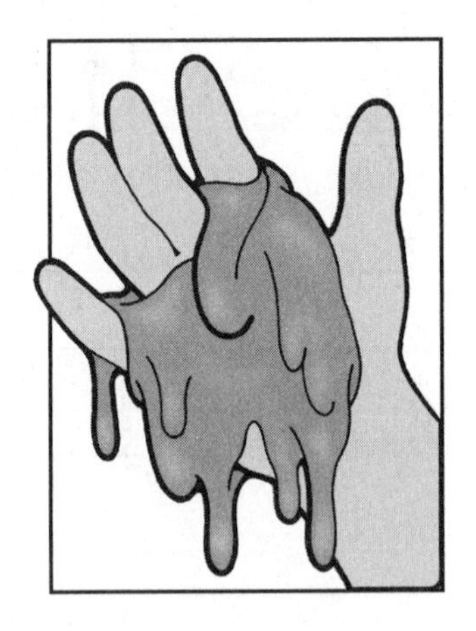

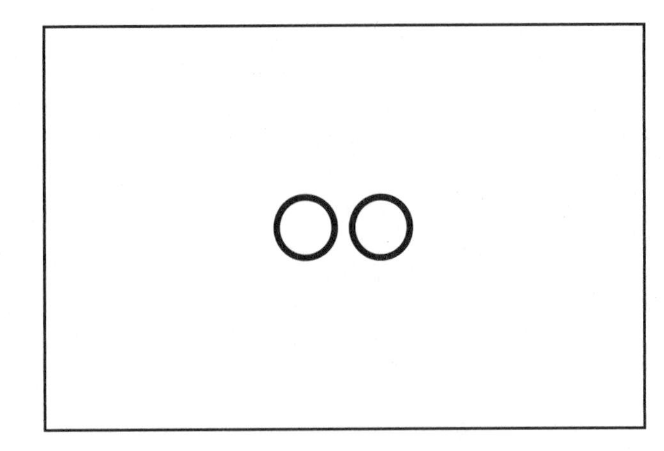

Practice A

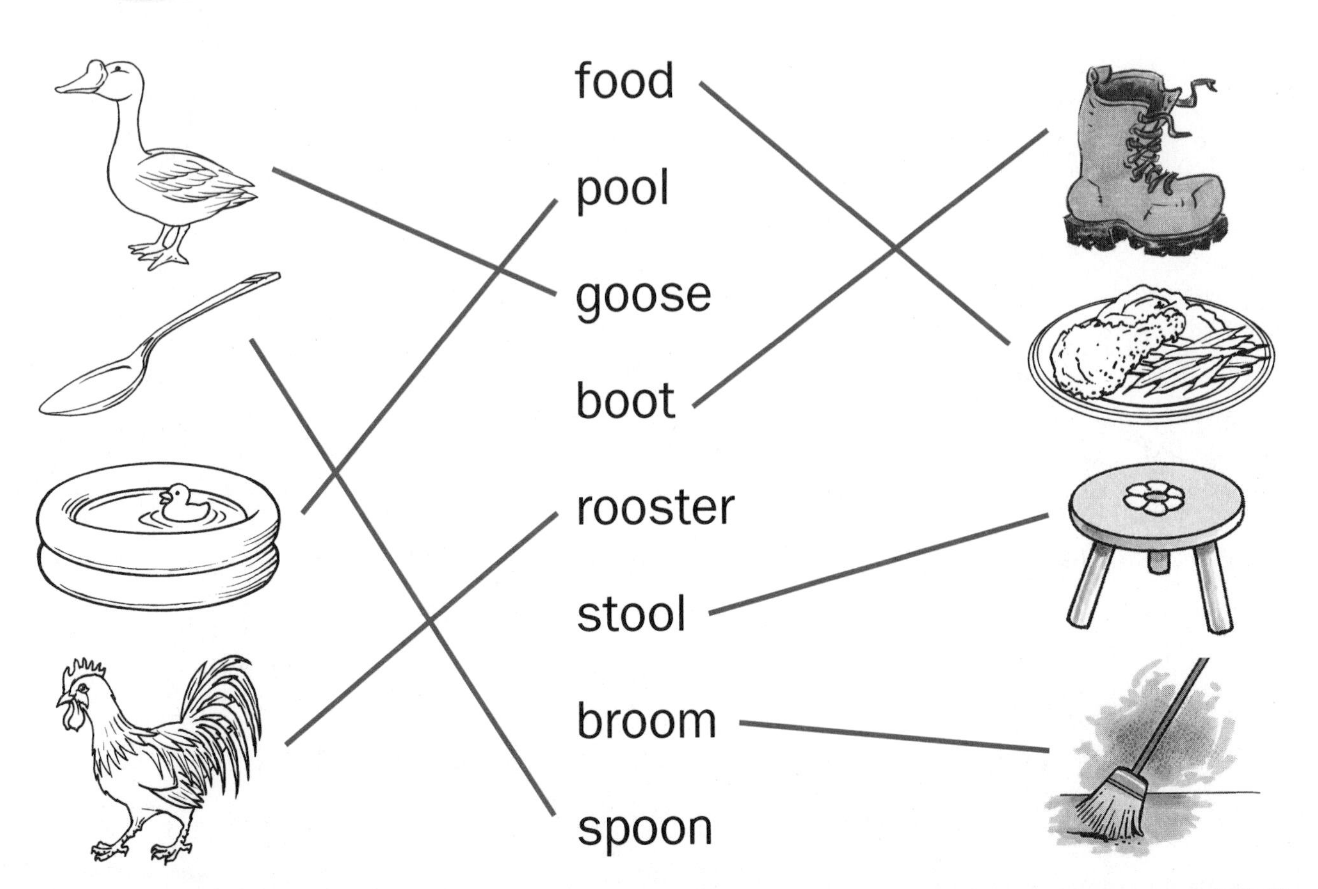

Practice B

At the top of the page, draw a line to connect the two words that go together. Write the compound words on the lines. At the bottom of the page, write the name of each picture.

1. bed — light
2. after — room
3. moon — noon

bedroom

afternoon

moonlight

4.

pool

5.

spoon

6.

tooth

Name ______________________________ Date __________

Sentences of Different Lengths

Directions: Read each sentence. Write the correct word to make it longer.

Focus When you write, write some short sentences and write some long sentences. You can add adjectives to make your sentences longer. You can combine two sentences to make one sentence.

Practice A

banana	fast	gray	green

1. The goat likes to eat green grass.
2. At the zoo, we will see gray hippos.
3. I like to run fast.
4. My dad likes to eat banana bread.

Practice B

Directions: Read both sentences. Combine them to make a longer sentence.

5. My cat is brown. My cat has white spots.

My cat is brown and has white spots.

6. Tim is tall. Tim has black hair.

Tim is tall and has black hair.

7. Leslie likes to play soccer. Leslie likes to read.

Leslie likes to play soccer and read.

Name ____________ Date ______

Sounds and Spellings

Directions: Write the spelling in the blanks to finish each word. Then read the words.

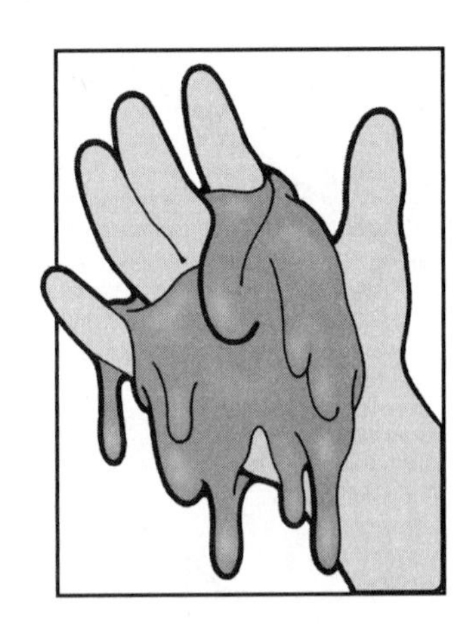

oo u
_ue

Practice A

1. 

sn o o ze

3. 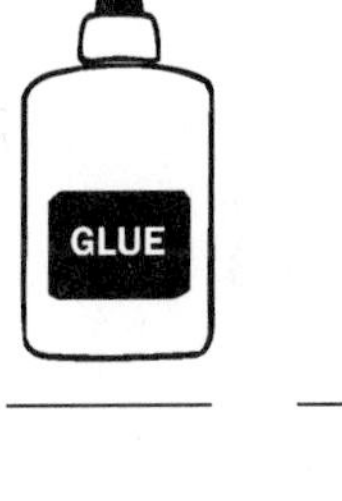

gl u e

2. 

st o o l

4. 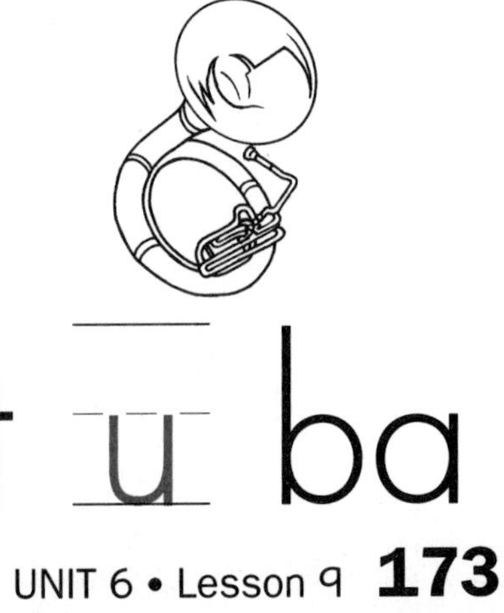

t u ba

Practice B

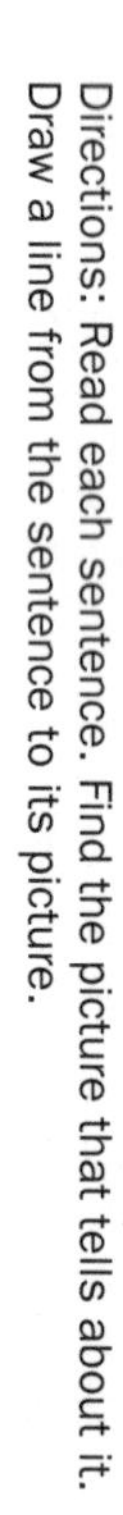

5. Use a ruler to make the line.

6. Boots scoots when it's time for his shampoo.

7. On Tuesdays I play the tuba.

8. Sue has the flu.

9. The superstar ate noodles and tuna.

Name ______________________ Date ________

Sounds and Spellings

Practice A

Directions: Draw a line to connect the two words that go together. Write the compound words on the lines.

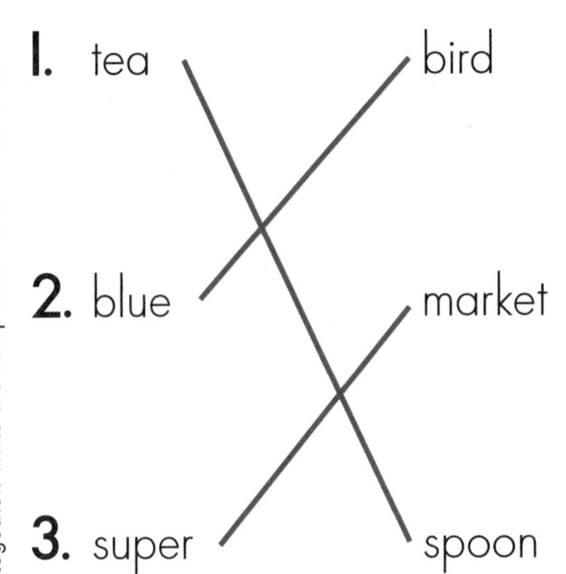

4. roof ——— top

teaspoon

bluebird

supermarket

rooftop

Practice B

Directions: At the top of the page, read the words in each box. Fill in the circle next to each word that has the /o͞o/ sound. At the bottom of the page, complete the sentence using the spellings represented by the ***Sound/Spelling Cards.***

6. ● snooze ● truth ○ snow

7. ○ black ● blue ● ruler

8. ● due ○ zone ● zoom

9. ● super ● tune ○ tone

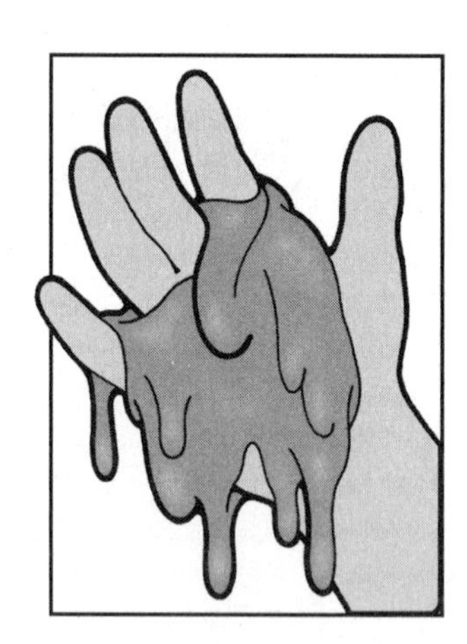

10. Julie has a loose tooth.

Name ______________________ Date ________

Directions: Copy the words in the spaces provided. Then, draw two pictures whose names have the /o͞o/ sound.

Sounds and Spellings

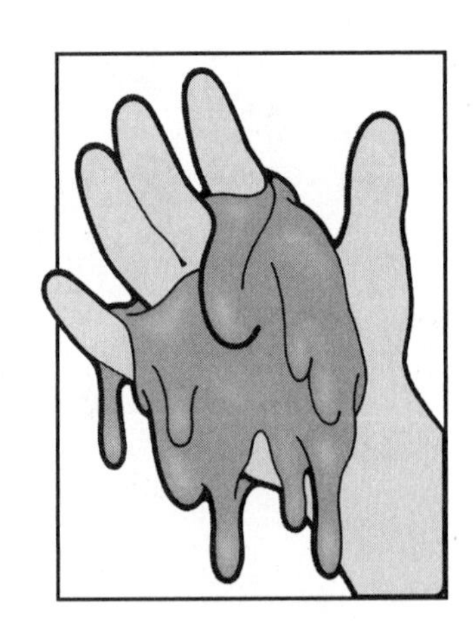

oo u_e
_ue _ew
u

Practice A

soon soon rude rude

clue clue blew blew

1. Answers will vary. Picture must contain the /o͞o/ sound.

2. Answers will vary. Picture must contain the /o͞o/ sound.

Practice B

Directions: Read each sentence. Circle the words with the /o͞o/ sound spelled *u, u_e, _ew, _ue,* or *oo.* Next say the name of each picture to the student. Then have the student write the name of each picture and underline the spelling of the /o͞o/ sound.

3. Dad has a new set of tools.

4. In June Sue went to the zoo.

5. Luke plays the tuba at noon.

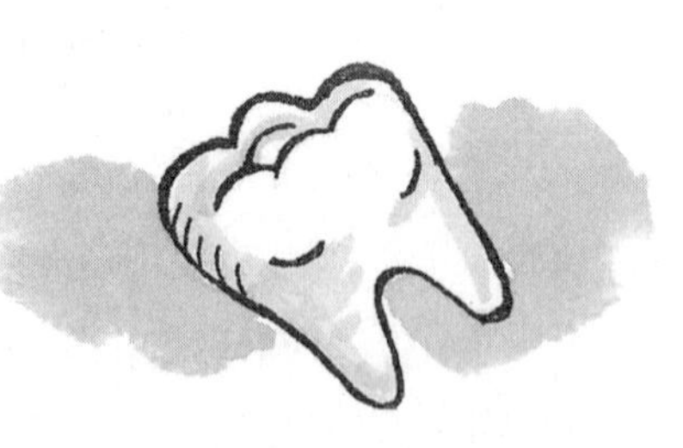

6. moon

7. stool

8. tooth

Name ______________________________ **Date** ________

Commas in a Series

Focus

Rule Commas are used in lists of three or more.

Example I like apples, bananas, and pears.

Practice A

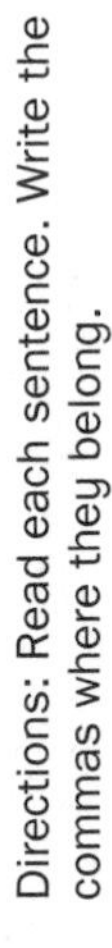

1. Tammy, Joel, Molly, and Andrew went for a picnic.

2. Molly brought plates, cups, and napkins.

3. Joel carried the picnic basket, drinks, and blanket.

4. The children ate bread, cheese, and bananas.

Practice B

Directions: Have students read the sentence frames. Then have them write three or more things in a series on the blanks. Remind them to use commas to separate each thing.

5. At the store, we got Possible Answers: milk, bread, and apples.

6. I went to a party and played Possible Answers: basketball, tag, and board games.

7. Possible Answers: Janet, Sam, and Tom are three of my classmates.

8. For our trip, I packed Possible Answers: clothes, shoes, and toys.

Name ______________________ Date ________

Sounds and Spellings

Directions: Practice writing oo. Copy the words. Then draw two pictures whose names have the /oo/ sound.

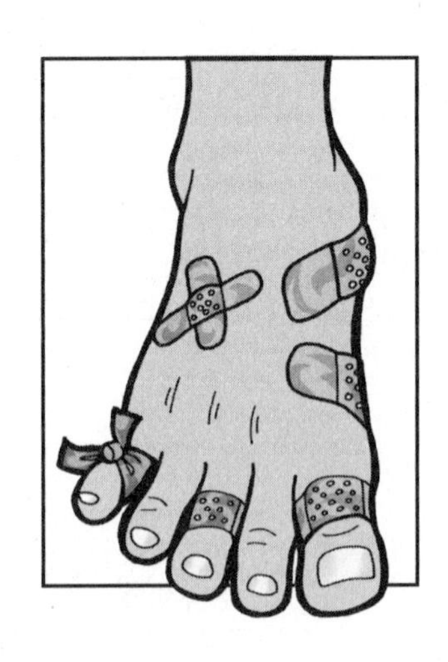

oo

Practice A

oo oo oo oo oo

look look wood wood

1. Answers will vary. Picture must contain the /oo/ sound.

2. Answers will vary. Picture must contain the /oo/ sound.

Practice B

Directions: Circle the sentence that tells about the picture.

3.

Luke has a good book.

Luke stood in line.

4.

Fish splash in a brook.

Fred soaks his foot.

5.

Sam fixes the hook.

Sam stacks wood.

Name ______________________ Date ________

Sounds and Spellings

Practice A

Directions: Read the words in the box. Write the correct word under each picture.

spool	book	chew	broom

1\.

book

2\.

spool

3\.

broom

4\.

chew

Practice B

Directions: Read each sentence. Fill in the circle by the word that completes each sentence.

5. You can fix it with super ______.

● glue ○ blue

6. Please sit on the wooden ______.

○ stole ● stool

7. Judy swims in a large ______.

● pool ○ spool

8. Bruce got a fish on his ______.

● hook ○ hood

9. Stu played the flute in the ______ band.

○ stood ● school